ZETA MATHS
www.zetamaths.com

4D+S

© 2018 M Mackison

This edition first published by Zeta Maths Limited, 2018.

Reprinted in 2019 by Bell & Bain Ltd.

ISBN 978-1-5272-3506-9

Acknowledgements:

The author would like to acknowledge and thank Gordon Stewart for his invaluable editorial advice. Also, special thanks to Erin Beveridge and Kirstin West for proof reading and checking of the manuscript.

Introduction

To become accomplished at anything in life takes hard work and effort. Few people are naturally gifted in any area, whether that be in sports, music or academic pursuits. And even for those who are, if they want to be the very best they can be, they need to work hard. The musician puts in hours of practice with scales and finger drills, so that they can play the most difficult pieces of music. The sprinter spends hours in the gym strengthening individual muscles, so that they can run the 100m as fast as possible. The footballer spends hours at training with passing drills, so that they can perform well on the field. In each case, the hard work is done in advance, so that when it matters, the skills and strengths are all there.

This book is a bit like that scales and finger drills book, or the gym exercises, or the passing drills. It has been written to develop skills and strengths in Algebra, so that the learner can put these into practice when it matters, be that in an exam or in more complex mathematical situations.

Often times these skills are not an end in themselves, but rather pave the way for learners to advance in their mathematical competence.

How to use this book

Within each chapter, exercises are differentiated by number. The exercises that begin with a **1** develop the more basic skills. The exercises that begin with a **2** develop skills towards GCSE and National 5 level. The exercises that begin with a **3** are for A-Level and Higher preparation.

Contents

Chapter 1
Simplifying Expressions 1

1.1 Basic Addition and Subtraction

Consider $2x + 3y$, this is called an **algebraic expression**. Within this expression, $2x$ is an **algebraic term**, where 2 is the **coefficient** and x is a **variable**.

When adding and subtracting terms within an algebraic expression, the terms that have the *same variable* go together.

Worked Examples:

1. $a + a + a + a = 4a$
2. $a + a + b + b + b = 2a + 3b$
3. $a + a + b - a = a + b$

Exercise 1.1

Simplify the following:

1. $a + a$
2. $b + b + b$
3. $c + c + c + c + c$

4. $d + d + d + d$
5. $e + e + e + e$
6. $f + f + f + f + f + f$

7. $g + g + g + g + g$
8. $h + h$
9. $i + i + i + i + i + i$

10. $j + j + j$
11. $k + k + k + k + k + k + k$
12. $l + l + l + l + l + l + l + l$

13. $a + a + a + b + b$
14. $c + c + d + d + c$
15. $e + e + f + f + f + f + e$

16. $g + h + g + g + h + h$
17. $j + j + k + k + j$
18. $m + n + m + n + m + m + n$

19. $a + b + a + a + b$
20. $c + c + d + c + d + d$
21. $e + e + e + f + e + f + e + f$

22. $g + h + h + h + g$
23. $j + k + j + k + k$
24. $a + c + b + b + c + a$

25. $a + a + a - a$
26. $b - b + b$
27. $c + c - c + c + c$

28. $d - d + d - d$
29. $e + e + e + e - e - e - e$
30. $f - f + f + f + f + f - f$

31. $a + b + a + a - b$
32. $c + c - d + c - d - d$
33. $e + e + e - f - e + f - e + f$

34. $g + h + h + h - g$
35. $-j - k - j - k + k$
36. $a - c + b - b + c - a$

1.2 Further Addition and Subtraction

Worked Examples:

1. $2a + 3a = 5a$
2. $3a + 5b + 2b = 3a + 7b$
3. $5a + 1 - 4a - 2 = a - 1$

NB: When adding and subtracting algebraic terms that include numbers with no algebraic term (as in example 3), the numbers are treated as normal.

Exercise 1.2

Simplify the following:

1. $3a + a$
2. $2b + 4b$
3. $4c + 3c$

4. $5d + 4d + 3d$
5. $3e + 5e + e$
6. $6f + f + 3f + 2f$

7. $5a + 2b + 3a + b$
8. $6c + 5d + d + 8c$
9. $11e + 12f + f + 10f + 6e$

10. $g + 10h + g + 10g + h$
11. $8j + 17j + 5k + 100k$
12. $14m + n + 5p + 5n + 8p + n$

13. $6a - 3a$
14. $7b - 5b$
15. $8c + 2c - 7c$

16. $12d - 11d + 4d$
17. $14e + 8e - 7e$
18. $7f - 9f$

19. $4a + 3b - 2a - b$
20. $5c - 2d + c - d$
21. $9e + 5f - 10e + f$

22. $8g - 2h - 5g + h$
23. $6j + 2k - 7j - k$
24. $3a - 2b + c + 4a - 6b - 4c$

25. $2x + 4y - 5 - x + 6y$
26. $4c + 2 - 3d + 5 - 2c - d$
27. $5r - 3s + 9 - 3r + 5s - 11$

28. $6p + 9q - 8 + 5p - 12q + 5$
29. $2m - 3n + 9 - 7n + 2m - 2$
30. $4x - 3y - 8x + 5 - 2y - 8$

1.3 Multiplication of Algebraic Terms by Numbers

When multiplying an algebraic term by a number, multiply the **coefficient** of the algebraic term by the number.

NB: If a term has no explicit numerical part (no number in front of the letter), the coefficient is 1. **E.g.** x has a coefficient of 1.

Worked Examples:

1. $a \times 3 = 3a$
2. $2b \times 5 = 10b$
3. $4 \times 7c = 28c$

Exercise 1.3

Simplify the following:

1. $a \times 5$
2. $b \times 6$
3. $c \times 7$
4. $d \times 8$

5. $9 \times e$
6. $13 \times f$
7. $4g \times 2$
8. $7h \times 3$

9. $9i \times 4$
10. $10j \times 2$
11. $4k \times 3$
12. $7 \times 2l$

13. $6m \times 4$
14. $5n \times 3$
15. $6 \times 3p$
16. $4 \times 3q$

17. $8r \times 8$
18. $7 \times 2s$
19. $12 \times 3t$
20. $2u \times 13$

21. $6 \times 7v$
22. $x \times 2 \times 3$
23. $3y \times 4 \times 2$
24. $6 \times 2z \times 5$

1.4 Multiplication of Algebraic Terms by Letters

Worked Examples:

1. $a \times b = ab$ **2.** $c \times d \times e = cde$ **3.** $h \times h = h^2$

Exercise 1.4

Simplify the following:

1. $a \times b$
2. $b \times c$
3. $a \times c$
4. $b \times d$

5. $e \times f \times g$
6. $g \times d$
7. $k \times m$
8. $t \times r \times s$

9. $n \times n$
10. $m \times m$
11. $g \times b \times b$
12. $w \times r \times w$

1.5 Multiplication of Algebraic Terms by Letters and Numbers

When multiplying algebraic terms together; multiply the coefficients together and multiply the variables together.

Worked Examples:

1. $2a \times 3b = 6ab$ **2.** $4c \times 2d \times 3e = 24cde$ **3.** $3y \times 5y = 15y^2$

Exercise 1.5

Simplify the following:

1. $3a \times b$
2. $g \times 5c$
3. $5h \times 2c$
4. $9a \times 2d$

5. $e \times 2f \times 3g$
6. $8e \times 5d$
7. $h \times 2m$
8. $9n \times 3e$

9. $2c \times 6ab$
10. $4s \times 2tu$
11. $3cv \times 3ds$
12. $6t \times 2t$

13. $4m \times 3m$
14. $5b \times 3b$
15. $6a \times 3ab$
16. $4bc \times 3cd$

17. $5r \times 8r$
18. $7bv \times 2sv$
19. $2ab \times 3ab$
20. $2wz \times 4wz$

21. $6r \times 2pr$
22. $x \times 2x \times 3v$
23. $4b \times 4b \times 2c$
24. $5g \times 2dg \times 5d$

1.6 Mixed Simplifying 1 – Use of BIDMAS

In questions that involve more than one operation, it is necessary to consider the order of operations. Use BIDMAS (Brackets, Indices, Division, Multiplication, Addition, Subtraction).

Worked Examples:

1. $5a + 2a \times 3$
$= 5a + 6a$
$= 11a$

2. $4b \times 2b + 3b$
$= 4b^2 + 3b$

3. $3w \times 2w - 4w \times w$
$= 6w^2 - 4w^2$
$= 2w^2$

Exercise 1.6

Simplify the following:

1. $a + a \times 2$
2. $b + b \times 3$
3. $c + c \times 5$
4. $3d + d \times 4$

5. $2e - 5 \times e$
6. $5f - 2f \times 2$
7. $6g - 3g \times 3$
8. $4 \times h - h$

9. $5 \times i - 3i$
10. $6 \times j + 4j$
11. $k \times 3 + 3k$
12. $4m + m \times 5$

13. $6n - 3n \times 2$
14. $3 \times p + p \times 4$
15. $3 \times q + 4 \times q$
16. $r \times 5 + 6 \times r$

17. $2r \times 5r - 2r \times r$
18. $3s \times s - s \times 5s$
19. $5wx - w \times 2x$
20. $5wy - 2y \times 3w$

21. $z - 2z \times 7$
22. $3a \times 5 - a$
23. $b - b \times 3$
24. $3c - c \times 4$

25. $10d - 2d \times 7$
26. $3e \times 5 - 2 \times e$
27. $5f + 3f \times 2$
28. $7g - g \times 3$

1.7 Division of Algebraic Terms by Letters and Numbers

In these types of questions, divide the *coefficients* by the *coefficients* and the *variables* by the *variables*.

Worked Examples:

1. $\dfrac{a}{2a} = \dfrac{1}{2}$
2. $abc \div ab = \dfrac{abc}{ab} = c$
3. $\dfrac{6xy}{2y} = \dfrac{3x}{1} = 3x$
4. $\dfrac{bc}{bc^2} = \dfrac{b \times c}{b \times c \times c} = \dfrac{1}{c}$

Exercise 1.7

Simplify the following:

1. $\dfrac{a}{6a}$
2. $\dfrac{5b}{b}$
3. $\dfrac{2c}{c}$
4. $\dfrac{d}{4d}$
5. $\dfrac{3}{6e}$

6. $\dfrac{f}{5f}$
7. $\dfrac{g}{6g}$
8. $\dfrac{8h}{h}$
9. $\dfrac{4}{2r}$
10. $5h \div 5$

11. $\dfrac{6}{3j}$
12. $\dfrac{6m}{8}$
13. $8q \div q$
14. $\dfrac{5r}{10}$
15. $\dfrac{12}{16n}$

16. $\dfrac{a}{3a}$
17. $\dfrac{2b}{b}$
18. $\dfrac{5c}{10c}$
19. $\dfrac{d}{3d}$
20. $\dfrac{4e}{8e}$

21. $\dfrac{10f}{5f}$
22. $\dfrac{12g}{15g}$
23. $\dfrac{20h}{60h}$
24. $\dfrac{42r}{21r}$
25. $gh \div g$

26. $\dfrac{j}{jk}$
27. $\dfrac{mnp}{mn}$
28. $qrs \div qs$
29. $\dfrac{tw}{tvw}$
30. $\dfrac{z}{xyz}$

31. $4ab \div 2b$
32. $\dfrac{5b}{10bc}$
33. $\dfrac{21c}{14cd}$
34. $\dfrac{8de}{4def}$
35. $\dfrac{4gk}{12ghk}$

36. $\dfrac{20xy}{100y}$ 37. $\dfrac{24abc}{16ac}$ 38. $\dfrac{xy^2}{xy}$ 39. $\dfrac{ab}{a^2b}$ 40. $\dfrac{5bc^2}{25c}$

41. $\dfrac{18def}{9d^2e}$ 42. $\dfrac{50ab^2c}{25ac^2}$ 43. $\dfrac{27x^2y^2}{18xy^2}$ 44. $\dfrac{60s^2tu^2}{40st^2u}$ 45. $\dfrac{24mn^2}{27m^2n^2p}$

1.8 Mixed Simplifying 2 – The Four Operations

Exercise 1.8

Simplify the following:

1. $3a + 2a$
2. $2b \times 5b$
3. $6c + 3c$
4. $9a + 2b - 4a$

5. $2d \times 3g$
6. $8e - 5e$
7. $r \times 2rm$
8. $\dfrac{3d^2}{d}$

9. $2t \times 2rs$
10. $5s + 2t - 3s + t$
11. $4xy \div 2x$
12. $6g \times 2g$

13. $2mn \times 2np$
14. $3a - 5a$
15. $6z + 3x - 4z - 3x$
16. $4a + 2 - 3 \times a$

17. $5 + 2 \times x + 4x$
18. $8bv \div 2v$
19. $\dfrac{2ab}{4abc}$
20. $2wz \times 4wz$

21. $6r \times 2pr$
22. $x \times 2x \times 3v$
23. $4b \times 4b \times 2c$
24. $5g \times 2g - 3g^2$

25. $6 \times b - 3b + 2$
26. $(-b) \times b$
27. $3c + 4c - 7c$
28. $9ad \div 3a$

29. $3xy \times 2x$
30. $6yz^2 \times 2y$
31. $\dfrac{12ab^2c}{4abc}$
32. $9e - 3e + 4f$

33. $7p \div 7p$
34. $4s + 8s - 3 \times 2s$
35. $5 \times 4v - 2v$
36. $6s - 9s \div 3$

37. $3h - 5h \times 2$
38. $2 \times 6t - 5t$
39. $12e + 15e \div 3$
40. $3w \times (-w)$

41. $2sr \times (-5)$
42. $4vw \times (-2v)$
43. $\dfrac{5k \times 4m}{10m}$
44. $(-2z) \times (-3z)$

45. $(-4r) \times (-5rs)$
46. $5 \times 2y - 4y$
47. $13a^2 - 2a \times 4a$
48. $-e \times (-e) \times (-3)$

2.1 Further Multiplication of Terms – The First Law of Indices

In the term $4x^3$, x is the **base** and 3 is the **power** or **index**. When two algebraic terms of the *same base* are multiplied, the powers are *added*. This is the first law of indices: $a^x \times a^y = a^{x+y}$

Worked Examples:

1. $a \times a = a^{1+1} = a^2$

2. $b^2 \times b^3 = b^{2+3} = b^5$

3. $4c^5 \times 5c^{-2} = 20c^{5+(-2)} = 20c^3$

NB: $a^0 = 1$ and $a^1 = a$

Exercise 2.1

Simplify the following:

1. $a \times a$

2. $b \times b$

3. $c \times c^2$

4. $d^2 \times d^3$

5. $e^3 \times e^3$

6. $f^2 \times f^3$

7. $g^4 \times g^5$

8. $h^6 \times h^2$

9. $j^4 \times j^9$

10. $k^{11} \times k^{12}$

11. $m^5 \times m^2$

12. $n^6 \times n^4$

13. $p^{15} \times p^3 \times p^7$

14. $q^8 \times q^{-2}$

15. $r^7 \times r^{-3}$

16. $s^5 \times s^{-1}$

17. $t^{-3} \times t^7$

18. $3u^7 \times 2u^3$

19. $4v^{12} \times 5v^{10}$

20. $6w^{15} \times 4w^6$

21. $6x^4 \times 12x^8$

22. $11y^9 \times 3y^7$

23. $15z^{12} \times 2z^{-3}$

24. $12e^{11} \times 12e^{-5}$

25. $15a^{-3} \times 2a^{-7}$

26. $9b^{13} \times 4b^5$

27. $11c^{22} \times 5c^{21}$

28. $18d^{-1} \times 4d$

29. $12e \times 10e^{-4}$

30. $9s^6 \times 4s^{-7}$

31. $5x^8 \times 2x^{-7}$

32. $11z \times 2z \times 2z^{-2}$

2.2 Further Division of Terms – The Second Law of Indices

When two algebraic terms of the *same base* are divided, the powers are *subtracted*. This is the second law of indices: $\dfrac{a^x}{a^y} = a^{x-y}$

Worked Examples:

1. $\dfrac{a^2}{a} = a^{2-1} = a$

2. $\dfrac{b^8}{b^2} = b^{8-2} = b^6$

3. $\dfrac{2c^5}{4c^2} = \dfrac{c^{5-2}}{2} = \dfrac{c^3}{2}$

4. $\dfrac{3c^4}{3c^4} = c^{4-4} = c^0 = 1.$

NB: In example 4, it is evident that the same numerator and denominator simplify to 1. Therefore, this example shows that anything to the power zero is equal to 1.

Exercise 2.2

Simplify the following:

1. $\dfrac{a^3}{a}$

2. $\dfrac{b^2}{b}$

3. $c^4 \div c^2$

4. $\dfrac{d^5}{d^4}$

5. $\dfrac{e^8}{e^5}$

6. $f^{10} \div f^5$

7. $\dfrac{g^{16}}{g^{12}}$

8. $\dfrac{h^{11}}{h^7}$

9. $\dfrac{j^{21}}{j^2}$

10. $\dfrac{k^{16}}{k^5}$

11. $\dfrac{m^8}{m^3}$ 12. $\dfrac{n^{14}}{n^{10}}$ 13. $\dfrac{p^{15}}{p^8}$ 14. $\dfrac{q^{25}}{q^{25}}$ 15. $r^{33} \div r^{22}$

16. $\dfrac{12s^5}{6s^2}$ 17. $22t^7 \div 2t^5$ 18. $\dfrac{4u^{13}}{8u^{11}}$ 19. $\dfrac{7v^{23}}{21v^{16}}$ 20. $\dfrac{12w^{31}}{16w^{22}}$

21. $\dfrac{x^3y^4}{x^2y^2}$ 22. $\dfrac{w^7x^4}{w^5x^3}$ 23. $\dfrac{c^{10}d^8}{c^3d^5}$ 24. $e^6g^4 \div e^3g^4$ 25. $\dfrac{m^9n^6p^4}{m^2n^3p}$

26. $\dfrac{27d^3e^5f}{9d^2ef}$ 27. $\dfrac{16ab^8c^5}{24ab^6c^2}$ 28. $\dfrac{2x^4y^2z}{18x^3y^2}$ 29. $\dfrac{60s^7t^8u^9}{80st^7u}$ 30. $\dfrac{24m^2n^2p}{36m^2n^2p}$

2.3 Combination of First and Second Laws of Indices

Worked Examples:

1. $\dfrac{a^2 \times a}{a} = \dfrac{a^3}{a} = a^{3-1} = a^2$ 2. $\dfrac{2x^2 \times x^4}{6x^3} = \dfrac{2x^6}{6x^3} = \dfrac{x^3}{3}$ 3. $\dfrac{2r^4 \times 6r}{3r \times 2r} = \dfrac{12r^5}{6r^2} = 2r^3$

Exercise 2.3

Simplify the following:

1. $\dfrac{a^3 \times a^2}{a}$ 2. $\dfrac{b \times b^2}{b}$ 3. $\dfrac{c^5 \times c^3}{c^2}$ 4. $\dfrac{d^3 \times d}{d^4}$ 5. $\dfrac{e^2 \times e^4}{e^5}$

6. $\dfrac{3f^3 \times 2f^2}{4f}$ 7. $\dfrac{4g^5 \times 3g^3}{2g^2}$ 8. $\dfrac{6h^6 \times 3h^2}{2h^5}$ 9. $\dfrac{2j^2 \times 3j^3}{12j^4}$ 10. $\dfrac{2k^4 \times k^5}{4k^6}$

11. $\dfrac{m^4 \times 3m^{-2}}{9m^2}$ 12. $\dfrac{6n^2 \times n}{3n^3 \times 3n^3}$ 13. $\dfrac{2p^2 \times 4p^2}{p^3 \times 12p}$ 14. $\dfrac{5q \times 3q^3}{12q^5 \times 2q}$ 15. $\dfrac{2r^6}{4r^5 \times 4r^5}$

16. $\dfrac{12s^8}{3s^2 \times 8s^3}$ 17. $\dfrac{3t^2 \times 5t^{-2}}{5t^3 \times 2t^3}$ 18. $\dfrac{2u^3 \times 6u^{-2}}{3u^3 \times 12u}$ 19. $\dfrac{6v^4 \times 4v^{-1}}{3v^5 \times 2v^{-2}}$ 20. $\dfrac{8w^3 \times 5w^6}{4w^9 \times 20w^{-5}}$

2.4 Raising Powers to Powers – The Third Law of Indices

When an algebraic term containing a power is raised to a power, the powers are *multiplied*. This is the third law of indices. $(a^x)^y = a^{xy}$

Worked Examples:

1. $(2a)^3 = 2^3 a^{1 \times 3} = 8a^3$ 2. $(b^4)^3 = b^{4 \times 3} = b^{12}$ 3. $(3c^3)^2 = 3^2 c^{3 \times 2} = 9c^6$

Exercise 2.4

Simplify the following:

1. $(a^2)^2$
2. $(b^3)^2$
3. $(c^3)^3$
4. $(d^4)^3$
5. $(e^5)^3$

6. $(f^4)^5$
7. $(g^7)^3$
8. $(h^2)^8$
9. $(i^7)^6$
10. $(j^5)^{-2}$

11. $(k^{12})^2$
12. $(l^{11})^5$
13. $(m^{-4})^3$
14. $(n^{18})^{-1}$
15. $(p^{15})^3$

16. $(xy^2)^2$
17. $(x^2y)^2$
18. $(x^3y^2)^2$
19. $(x^4yz^2)^3$
20. $(x^5y^4z^2)^4$

21. $(2z)^2$
22. $(3x)^2$
23. $(4r)^2$
24. $(3s)^3$
25. $(4t)^3$

26. $(5a)^3$
27. $(2u)^4$
28. $(3v)^4$
29. $(5y)^2$
30. $(6p)^3$

31. $(2y^2)^2$
32. $(3x^3)^2$
33. $(4g^4)^2$
34. $(3e^5)^3$
35. $(5k^6)^3$

36. $(2a^3b)^3$
37. $(2r^2u)^4$
38. $(3w^5v^3)^4$
39. $(5xy^6)^2$
40. $(6n^3p)^3$

2.5 Negative Indices – The Fourth Law of Indices

When an algebraic term has a negative power or index, this can be expressed as a *positive index* by moving the term from the numerator to the denominator or vice versa. This is the fourth law of indices: $a^{-x} = \dfrac{1}{a^x}$

Worked Examples:

1. $a^{-1} = \dfrac{1}{a^1} = \dfrac{1}{a}$

3. $2c^{-3} = \dfrac{2}{c^3}$

3. $\dfrac{d^{-2}}{2} = \dfrac{1}{2d^2}$

4. $(2e)^{-2} = \dfrac{1}{(2e)^2} = \dfrac{1}{4e^2}$

5. $(2f^3)^{-2} = \dfrac{1}{\left(2f^3\right)^2} = \dfrac{1}{4f^6}$

6. $\dfrac{2}{5g^{-2}} = \dfrac{2g^2}{5}$

Exercise 2.5

Express each term in positive index form:

1. x^{-1}
2. y^{-2}
3. z^{-3}
4. g^{-5}
5. r^{-4}

6. h^{-1}
7. w^{-7}
8. q^{-8}
9. p^{-2}
10. u^{-10}

11. $2r^{-1}$
12. $3p^{-2}$
13. $5e^{-5}$
14. $6t^{-3}$
15. $18n^{-6}$

16. $\dfrac{b^{-2}}{4}$
17. $\dfrac{d^{-6}}{2}$
18. $\dfrac{r^{-5}}{7}$
19. $\dfrac{y^{-4}}{3}$
20. $\dfrac{d^{-10}}{8}$

21. $\dfrac{5b^{-3}}{2}$
22. $\dfrac{2w^{-5}}{3}$
23. $\dfrac{5h^{-6}}{12}$
24. $\dfrac{11b^{-9}}{33}$
25. $\dfrac{16m^{-7}}{4}$

26. $(3a)^{-3}$
27. $(2u)^{-4}$
28. $(3v)^{-2}$
29. $(5y)^{-2}$
30. $(6p)^{-3}$

31. $(2y^2)^{-2}$ 32. $(3e^2)^{-2}$ 33. $(4t^3)^{-2}$ 34. $(3m^5)^{-3}$ 35. $(5r^6)^{-3}$

36. $\dfrac{5}{25b^{-3}}$ 37. $\dfrac{2}{11e^{-5}}$ 38. $\dfrac{8}{25b^{-3}}$ 39. $\dfrac{8}{12t^{-6}}$ 40. $\dfrac{42}{18r^{-3}}$

Express each term in negative index form:

41. $\dfrac{1}{a^3}$ 42. $\dfrac{1}{b^2}$ 43. $\dfrac{1}{c^5}$ 44. $\dfrac{1}{d^4}$ 45. $\dfrac{1}{e^7}$

46. $\dfrac{2}{f^4}$ 47. $\dfrac{3}{g^7}$ 48. $\dfrac{9}{h^6}$ 49. $\dfrac{14}{j}$ 50. $\dfrac{12}{k^8}$

51. $\dfrac{10}{2a^4}$ 52. $\dfrac{9}{3b^5}$ 53. $\dfrac{8}{4c^3}$ 54. $\dfrac{10}{15d^2}$ 55. $\dfrac{12}{4e^4}$

56. $\dfrac{22}{11f^8}$ 57. $\dfrac{4}{12g^2}$ 58. $\dfrac{15}{5h^3}$ 59. $\dfrac{6}{8j^5}$ 60. $\dfrac{12}{6k}$

2.6 Fractional Indices

When an algebraic term has a fractional power or index, the *denominator* (bottom number) of the index represents the root and the *numerator* (top number) represents the power: $a^{\frac{x}{y}} = \sqrt[y]{a^x}$

Worked Examples:

1. $a^{\frac{1}{2}} = \sqrt[2]{a^1} = \sqrt{a}$ **2.** $b^{-\frac{2}{3}} = \dfrac{1}{b^{\frac{2}{3}}} = \dfrac{1}{\sqrt[3]{b^2}}$ **3.** $\sqrt[6]{c^5} = c^{\frac{5}{6}}$ **4.** $\dfrac{1}{\sqrt[4]{d^3}} = d^{-\frac{3}{4}}$

Exercise 2.6

Express each term in root form:

1. $x^{\frac{1}{2}}$ 2. $y^{\frac{1}{3}}$ 3. $p^{\frac{1}{4}}$ 4. $r^{\frac{1}{5}}$ 5. $s^{\frac{1}{7}}$

6. $a^{\frac{3}{2}}$ 7. $b^{\frac{2}{3}}$ 8. $c^{\frac{4}{3}}$ 9. $d^{\frac{1}{6}}$ 10. $e^{\frac{5}{3}}$

11. $m^{\frac{2}{5}}$ 12. $n^{\frac{7}{3}}$ 13. $p^{\frac{7}{6}}$ 14. $q^{\frac{4}{9}}$ 15. $r^{\frac{8}{3}}$

16. $s^{\frac{6}{7}}$ 17. $t^{-\frac{1}{2}}$ 18. $u^{-\frac{2}{3}}$ 19. $v^{-\frac{4}{5}}$ 20. $w^{-\frac{6}{7}}$

Express each term in index form: **e.g.** (i) $\sqrt{x} = x^{\frac{1}{2}}$ (ii) $\dfrac{1}{\sqrt{a}} = x^{-\frac{1}{2}}$

21. $\sqrt{a}$ 22. $\sqrt{b}$ 23. $\sqrt{c^3}$ 24. $\sqrt{d^5}$ 25. $\sqrt{e^4}$

26. $\sqrt[3]{f^2}$ 27. $\sqrt[3]{g^4}$ 28. $\sqrt[4]{h^7}$ 29. $\sqrt[5]{j^3}$ 30. $\sqrt[3]{k^5}$

31. $\sqrt[4]{m^5}$

32. $\sqrt[4]{n^6}$

33. $\sqrt[3]{p^6}$

34. $\sqrt[2]{q^8}$

35. $\sqrt[4]{r^{12}}$

36. $\dfrac{1}{\sqrt{a}}$

37. $\dfrac{1}{\sqrt[3]{b}}$

38. $\dfrac{1}{\sqrt[4]{c}}$

39. $\dfrac{1}{\sqrt[5]{d}}$

40. $\dfrac{2}{\sqrt[3]{e}}$

41. $\dfrac{1}{\sqrt[3]{x^2}}$

42. $\dfrac{1}{\sqrt[4]{y^3}}$

43. $\dfrac{1}{\sqrt{z^3}}$

44. $\dfrac{1}{\sqrt[5]{g^3}}$

45. $\dfrac{1}{\sqrt[3]{h^2}}$

46. $\dfrac{2}{\sqrt[5]{e^3}}$

47. $\dfrac{3}{\sqrt[7]{b^2}}$

48. $\dfrac{5}{\sqrt[3]{t^5}}$

49. $\dfrac{9}{\sqrt[2]{c^8}}$

50. $\dfrac{10}{\sqrt[4]{k^5}}$

2.7 Mixed Simplifying 3 – Indices

Exercise 2.7

Express each term in positive index form and in root form where appropriate:

1. $a^{\frac{1}{2}} \times a^{\frac{1}{2}}$

2. $r^{\frac{1}{2}} \times r^{\frac{3}{2}}$

3. $s^{\frac{2}{3}} \times s^{\frac{2}{3}}$

4. $p^{\frac{1}{2}} \times p^{\frac{3}{4}}$

5. $k^{\frac{1}{2}} \times k^{-\frac{1}{2}}$

6. $m^{\frac{1}{2}} \times m^3$

7. $s^{\frac{1}{5}} \times s^{-\frac{2}{5}}$

8. $j^3 \times j^{-\frac{1}{3}}$

9. $a^{\frac{1}{2}} \div a^{\frac{1}{2}}$

10. $d^{\frac{1}{2}} \div d^{\frac{1}{3}}$

11. $d^{\frac{3}{4}} \div d^2$

12. $d^{\frac{2}{5}} \div d^{-\frac{1}{2}}$

13. $\dfrac{t^{\frac{1}{4}}}{t}$

14. $\dfrac{6x^{\frac{1}{2}}}{x^2}$

15. $\dfrac{5y^2}{10y^{\frac{2}{3}}}$

16. $\dfrac{z^3}{\sqrt[3]{z^2}}$

17. $\dfrac{a^2}{\sqrt[4]{a^3}}$

18. $\dfrac{c}{\sqrt[4]{c^5}}$

19. $\dfrac{6\sqrt{s}}{\sqrt[3]{s^4}}$

20. $\dfrac{5\sqrt{v^3}}{10v^2}$

21. $\left(2x^{\frac{1}{2}}\right)^3$

22. $\left(3a^{\frac{2}{3}}\right)^2$

23. $\left(4b^{\frac{1}{4}}\right)^3$

24. $\left(5c^{\frac{2}{3}}\right)^3$

Chapter 2
Expanding Brackets

1.1 Expanding Single Brackets

To expand brackets, the term on the outside of the bracket multiplies each term inside the bracket:

$$a(b + c) = ab + ac$$

Worked Examples:

1. $3(x + 5)$
   $= 3x + 15$

2. $4(x + y)$
   $= 4x + 4y$

3. $3x(2x + 7)$
   $= 6x^2 + 21x$

4. $2(x + 4) + 2$
   $= 2x + 8 + 2$
   $= 2x + 10$

Exercise 1.1

Expand the following, simplify where possible:

1. $a(b + c)$
2. $c(d + e)$
3. $d(e + f)$
4. $e(f + g)$

5. $a(b + 2)$
6. $b(c + 5)$
7. $d(e + 9)$
8. $e(5 + f)$

9. $g(g + h)$
10. $h(k + h)$
11. $2(j + k)$
12. $5(p + q)$

13. $6(m + n)$
14. $7(p + r)$
15. $11(w + s)$
16. $9(e + v)$

17. $4(e + 6)$
18. $8(x + 4)$
19. $3(t + 9)$
20. $12(e + 3)$

21. $7(p + 3)$
22. $10(a + 5)$
23. $4(2w + 6)$
24. $5(2r + 3)$

25. $8(4c + 1)$
26. $9(5h + 4)$
27. $8(3 + 4c)$
28. $5(1 + 9p)$

29. $6(2b + 3e)$
30. $6(6x + 7)$
31. $4a(a + 2)$
32. $3x(x + 6)$

33. $2g(g + 3)$
34. $5t(t + 8)$
35. $8d(d + 5c)$
36. $6y(2y + 3x)$

37. $4(b + 5) + 2$
38. $5(d + 2) + 6$
39. $6(g + 3) + 2g$
40. $7(h + 4) + 13$

41. $2(c + 7) + 5c$
42. $6(k + 5) + 2k$
43. $7(f + 9) + 18$
44. $3(d + 12) + 11$

45. $5a(a + 5) + 2a$
46. $5c(2c + 2) + 4c^2$
47. $3s(s + 2) + 5s^2$
48. $8a(2a + 4) + 6a$

1.2 Expanding Single Brackets with Negatives

To expand brackets, the term on the outside of the bracket multiplies each term inside the bracket:

$$a(b - c) = ab - ac$$

Worked Examples:

1. $3(x - 4)$
   $= 3x - 12$

2. $-6(x + y)$
   $= -6x - 6y$

3. $-3x(5x - 2)$
   $= -15x^2 + 6x$

4. $2 - 3(x + 4)$
   $= 2 - 3x - 12$
   $= -3x - 10$

Exercise 2.2

Expand and simplify:

1. $(a + 2)(a - 1)$

2. $(b + 3)(b - 5)$

3. $(c + 6)(c - 2)$

4. $(d + 1)(d - 3)$

5. $(e - 4)(e + 3)$

6. $(f - 5)(f + 2)$

7. $(g - 7)(g + 6)$

8. $(h + 3)(h - 1)$

9. $(j - 2)(j + 2)$

10. $(k + 4)(k - 4)$

11. $(m - 5)(m + 6)$

12. $(n + 3)(n - 3)$

13. $(p - 8)(p + 3)$

14. $(q - 7)(q + 3)$

15. $(r + 8)(r - 9)$

16. $(s + 5)(s - 10)$

17. $(t + 8)(t - 8)$

18. $(u + v)(u - v)$

19. $(2v + w)(v - 2w)$

20. $(w + 2x)(w - 3x)$

21. $(3x + 2y)(4x - 5y)$

22. $(2y + 2)(y - 2z)$

23. $(3x + 2y)(2x - 3z)$

24. $(4x - 3z)(2y + 2x)$

2.3 Multiplication of Two Brackets – Both Negative

Worked Examples:

1. $(a - 1)(a - 3)$
   $= a^2 - 3a - a + 3$
   $= a^2 - 4a + 3$

2. $(b - 5)(b - 2)$
   $= b^2 - 2b - 5b + 10$
   $= b^2 - 7b + 10$

3. $(c - 4)(c - 4)$
   $= c^2 - 4c - 4c + 16$
   $= c^2 - 8c + 16$

Exercise 2.3

Expand and simplify:

1. $(a - 3)(a - 1)$

2. $(b - 2)(b - 5)$

3. $(c - 1)(c - 2)$

4. $(d - 2)(d - 3)$

5. $(e - 4)(e - 5)$

6. $(f - 5)(f - 6)$

7. $(g - 7)(g - 2)$

8. $(h - 9)(h - 1)$

9. $(j - 2)(j - 2)$

10. $(k - 5)(k - 5)$

11. $(m - 3)(m - 3)$

12. $(n - 6)(n - 6)$

13. $(p - 8)(p - 1)$

14. $(q - 7)(q - 10)$

15. $(r - 3)(r - 9)$

16. $(s - 2)(s - 10)$

17. $(t - 4)(t - 8)$

18. $(u - v)(u - v)$

19. $(v - w)(v - 2w)$

20. $(2w - x)(w - 3x)$

21. $(5x - 2y)(x - 3y)$

22. $(2y - 3)(y - 2z)$

23. $(5x - 2y)(2x - 3z)$

24. $(7x - 3z)(2y - 2x)$

1.1 Expanding Single Brackets

To expand brackets, the term on the outside of the bracket multiplies each term inside the bracket:

$$a(b + c) = ab + ac$$

Worked Examples:

1. $3(x + 5)$	2. $4(x + y)$	3. $3x(2x + 7)$	4. $2(x + 4) + 2$
$= 3x + 15$	$= 4x + 4y$	$= 6x^2 + 21x$	$= 2x + 8 + 2$
			$= 2x + 10$

Exercise 1.1

Expand the following, simplify where possible:

1. $a(b + c)$
2. $c(d + e)$
3. $d(e + f)$
4. $e(f + g)$

5. $a(b + 2)$
6. $b(c + 5)$
7. $d(e + 9)$
8. $e(5 + f)$

9. $g(g + h)$
10. $h(k + h)$
11. $2(j + k)$
12. $5(p + q)$

13. $6(m + n)$
14. $7(p + r)$
15. $11(w + s)$
16. $9(e + v)$

17. $4(e + 6)$
18. $8(x + 4)$
19. $3(t + 9)$
20. $12(e + 3)$

21. $7(p + 3)$
22. $10(a + 5)$
23. $4(2w + 6)$
24. $5(2r + 3)$

25. $8(4c + 1)$
26. $9(5h + 4)$
27. $8(3 + 4c)$
28. $5(1 + 9p)$

29. $6(2b + 3e)$
30. $6(6x + 7)$
31. $4a(a + 2)$
32. $3x(x + 6)$

33. $2g(g + 3)$
34. $5t(t + 8)$
35. $8d(d + 5c)$
36. $6y(2y + 3x)$

37. $4(b + 5) + 2$
38. $5(d + 2) + 6$
39. $6(g + 3) + 2g$
40. $7(h + 4) + 13$

41. $2(c + 7) + 5c$
42. $6(k + 5) + 2k$
43. $7(f + 9) + 18$
44. $3(d + 12) + 11$

45. $5a(a + 5) + 2a$
46. $5c(2c + 2) + 4c^2$
47. $3s(s + 2) + 5s^2$
48. $8a(2a + 4) + 6a$

1.2 Expanding Single Brackets with Negatives

To expand brackets, the term on the outside of the bracket multiplies each term inside the bracket:

$$a(b - c) = ab - ac$$

Worked Examples:

1. $3(x - 4)$	2. $-6(x + y)$	3. $-3x(5x - 2)$	4. $2 - 3(x + 4)$
$= 3x - 12$	$= -6x - 6y$	$= -15x^2 + 6x$	$= 2 - 3x - 12$
			$= -3x - 10$

Exercise 1.2

Expand and simplify:

1. $a(b-c)$
2. $c(d-e)$
3. $d(e-f)$
4. $e(f-g)$

5. $a(b-3)$
6. $b(c-2)$
7. $d(e-1)$
8. $e(9-f)$

9. $g(g-2)$
10. $h(3-h)$
11. $-2(j+e)$
12. $-4(p+w)$

13. $-8(m+n)$
14. $-(p+r)$
15. $-2(w+s)$
16. $-6(e+v)$

17. $-2(e+6)$
18. $-7(x+4)$
19. $-3(t+9)$
20. $-20(e+3)$

21. $-2(p-3)$
22. $-10(a-5)$
23. $-3(2w-2)$
24. $-7(5r-2)$

25. $-3(2c-1)$
26. $-11(3h-3)$
27. $-3a(a-4)$
28. $-6b(b+p)$

29. $-c(2c-3)$
30. $6x(6x-7)$
31. $-2a(a+2)$
32. $-(x-6)$

33. $-3g(2g-3)$
34. $-2t(2t+3)$
35. $5d(d-5c)$
36. $-6y(2-3y)$

37. $4+(b-5)$
38. $5-(d+2)$
39. $6+4(g-3)$
40. $3-2(h-4)$

41. $4-(c+2)$
42. $-5(k-5)-25$
43. $-2(f+9)-12$
44. $-4(x+11)+4x$

45. $3a-2a(a-5)$
46. $5e-3e(2e+2)$
47. $3s^3-4s(s-2)$
48. $8a-4(2a-4)$

1.3 Addition or Subtraction of Two or More Brackets

When two or more brackets are being added or subtracted from one another, expand each bracket, then simplify:

Worked Examples:

1. $2(3x+4)+5(2x-3)$
   $=(6x+8)+(10x-15)$
   $=16x-7$

2. $3(2y-6)-4(3y+7)$
   $=6y-18-12y-28$
   $=-6y-46$

3. $4(2z+5)-(z-3)$
   $=8z+20-z+3$
   $=7z+23$

NB: In examples 2 and 3, the term outside the second bracket is negative.

Exercise 1.3

Expand and simplify:

1. $2(a+4)+3(a+2)$
2. $4(b-2)+3(b+5)$
3. $5(c-4)+7(c-5)$

4. $6(d+3)+3(d+8)$
5. $3(e-2)+5(e+6)$
6. $8(f+3)+6(f+7)$

7. $4(g-3)+9(g+2)$
8. $4h(h+3)+3h(h+1)$
9. $6j(2j-3)+2j(j+3)$

10. $3k(k+6)+2(k+5)$
11. $5m(m-1)+2(m+4)$
12. $7n(n-4)+3(n+10)$

13. $5(p - 1) - (p + 4)$

14. $.6(q + 2) - (q + 3)$

15. $3(r + 4) - (r + 5)$

16. $2(s - 3) - (s - 4)$

17. $7(t + 8) - (t - 11)$

18. $9(u + 5) - (u + 12)$

19. $2(v - 7) - 3(v + 4)$

20. $5(w - 1) - 3(w - 2)$

21. $11(x + 2) - 4(x + 7)$

22. $2y(y - 3) - 3(y - 4)$

23. $4z(z + 9) - 3(z - 8)$

24. $12(a - 5) - 7(a - 7)$

2.1 Multiplication of Two Brackets – Both Positive

When two brackets are multiplied together, multiply each term in the first bracket by each term in the second bracket. For this process we can use FOIL (Firsts Outsides Insides Lasts) or another suitable method,

e.g. $(x + 3)(x - 2) = x^2 - 2x + 3x - 6 = x^2 + x - 6$

Worked Examples:

1. $(a + 2)(a + 3)$
$= a^2 + 3a + 2a + 6$
$= a^2 + 5a + 6$

2. $(2b + 4)(3b + 5)$
$= 6b^2 + 10b + 12b + 20$
$= 6b^2 + 22b + 20$

3. $(c + 2d)(c + d)$
$= (c^2 + cd + 2cd + 2d^2)$
$= (c^2 + 3cd + 2d^2)$

Exercise 2.1

Expand and simplify:

1. $(a + 2)(a + 3)$

2. $(b + 1)(b + 5)$

3. $(c + 6)(c + 3)$

4. $(d + 1)(d + 1)$

5. $(e + 3)(e + 3)$

6. $(f + 6)(f + 2)$

7. $(g + 5)(g + 6)$

8. $(h + 3)(h + 9)$

9. $(j + 7)(j + 2)$

10. $(k + 7)(k + 5)$

11. $(m + 8)(m + 1)$

12. $(n + 1)(n + 1)$

13. $(p + 2)(p + 2)$

14. $(q + 5)(q + 5)$

15. $(r + 8)(r + 8)$

16. $(s + 11)(s + 3)$

17. $(2t + 1)(t + 3)$

18. $(3u + 5)(u + 3)$

19. $(5v + 2)(v + 1)$

20. $(2w + 1)(3w + 4)$

21. $(x + y)(x + z)$

22. $(2x + 3y)(3x + 2z)$

23. $(5x + 6y)(3x + 4y)$

24. $(7x + 4y)(5x + 3z)$

2.2 Multiplication of Two Brackets – One Negative

Worked Examples:

1. $(a + 2)(a - 3)$
$= a^2 - 3a + 2a - 6$
$= a^2 - a - 6$

2. $(b + 4)(b - 1)$
$= b^2 - b + 4b - 4$
$= b^2 + 3b - 4$

3. $(c + 6)(c - 6)$
$= c^2 - 6c + 6c - 36$
$= c^2 - 36$

Exercise 2.2

Expand and simplify:

1. $(a + 2)(a - 1)$
2. $(b + 3)(b - 5)$
3. $(c + 6)(c - 2)$

4. $(d + 1)(d - 3)$
5. $(e - 4)(e + 3)$
6. $(f - 5)(f + 2)$

7. $(g - 7)(g + 6)$
8. $(h + 3)(h - 1)$
9. $(j - 2)(j + 2)$

10. $(k + 4)(k - 4)$
11. $(m - 5)(m + 6)$
12. $(n + 3)(n - 3)$

13. $(p - 8)(p + 3)$
14. $(q - 7)(q + 3)$
15. $(r + 8)(r - 9)$

16. $(s + 5)(s - 10)$
17. $(t + 8)(t - 8)$
18. $(u + v)(u - v)$

19. $(2v + w)(v - 2w)$
20. $(w + 2x)(w - 3x)$
21. $(3x + 2y)(4x - 5y)$

22. $(2y + 2)(y - 2z)$
23. $(3x + 2y)(2x - 3z)$
24. $(4x - 3z)(2y + 2x)$

2.3 Multiplication of Two Brackets – Both Negative

Worked Examples:

1. $(a - 1)(a - 3)$
$= a^2 - 3a - a + 3$
$= a^2 - 4a + 3$

2. $(b - 5)(b - 2)$
$= b^2 - 2b - 5b + 10$
$= b^2 - 7b + 10$

3. $(c - 4)(c - 4)$
$= c^2 - 4c - 4c + 16$
$= c^2 - 8c + 16$

Exercise 2.3

Expand and simplify:

1. $(a - 3)(a - 1)$
2. $(b - 2)(b - 5)$
3. $(c - 1)(c - 2)$

4. $(d - 2)(d - 3)$
5. $(e - 4)(e - 5)$
6. $(f - 5)(f - 6)$

7. $(g - 7)(g - 2)$
8. $(h - 9)(h - 1)$
9. $(j - 2)(j - 2)$

10. $(k - 5)(k - 5)$
11. $(m - 3)(m - 3)$
12. $(n - 6)(n - 6)$

13. $(p - 8)(p - 1)$
14. $(q - 7)(q - 10)$
15. $(r - 3)(r - 9)$

16. $(s - 2)(s - 10)$
17. $(t - 4)(t - 8)$
18. $(u - v)(u - v)$

19. $(v - w)(v - 2w)$
20. $(2w - x)(w - 3x)$
21. $(5x - 2y)(x - 3y)$

22. $(2y - 3)(y - 2z)$
23. $(5x - 2y)(2x - 3z)$
24. $(7x - 3z)(2y - 2x)$

2.4 Multiplication of Two Brackets – Perfect Square Trinomials

A **perfect square trinomial** (see **chapter 3**, section 2.3 onwards) is the result of squaring a binomial. A **binomial** is an algebraic expression which is the sum or difference of two terms, such as $(x + y)$.

When squaring a binomial: square the first term, double the product or the terms and square the last term.

Worked Examples:

1. $(x + y)^2$
$= (x + y)(x + y)$
$= x^2 + 2xy + y^2$

2. $(x + 1)^2$
$= x^2 + 2(1x) + 1^2$
$= x^2 + 2x + 1$

3. $(x - 5)^2$
$= x^2 + 2(-5x) + 5^2$
$= x^2 - 10x + 25$

NB: Line two is for illustration and understanding of method. Lines 1 and 3 are the only required working.

Exercise 2.4

Square the following binomials to form perfect square trinomials:

1. $(a + b)^2$ *2.* $(b + c)^2$ *3.* $(c - d)^2$ *4.* $(d + 1)^2$

5. $(e - 1)^2$ *6.* $(f + 2)^2$ *7.* $(g - 2)^2$ *8.* $(h + 3)^2$

9. $(j - 3)^2$ *10.* $(k + 4)^2$ *11.* $(m - 4)^2$ *12.* $(n - 5)^2$

13. $(p + 6)^2$ *14.* $(q + 10)^2$ *15.* $(r - 7)^2$ *16.* $(s + 5)^2$

17. $(4 - x)^2$ *18.* $(5 + y)^2$ *19.* $(2x - 4)^2$ *20.* $(3y + 2z)^2$

2.5 Multiplication of Two Brackets – Mixed Exercise

Exercise 2.5

Expand and simplify:

1. $4(a - 1)$ *2.* $(b + 2)(b - 3)$ *3.* $(c + 6)^2$

4. $(d + 1)(d - 3)$ *5.* $2e(e + 4)$ *6.* $(f - 5)(f - 5)$

7. $(g + 6)(g - 6)$ *8.* $4h(h - 1)$ *9.* $(j + 2)^2$

10. $(k + 5)(k - 5)$ *11.* $(m - 7)(m + 6)$ *12.* $(n + 1)(n - 1)$

13. $(p - 8)(p + 5)$ *14.* $(q - 7)(q + 9)$ *15.* $(r + 8)(r - 10)$

16 $(s + 5)(s - 1)$ *17.* $(t + 10)(t - 10)$ *18.* $(u + 7)(u - 7)$

19. $(a + 5)(a - 2)$ *20.* $(b + 2)(b + 3)$ *21.* $(c - 8)(c - 5)$

22. $(d - 9)(d + 8)$ *23.* $(e - 10)(e - 10)$ *24.* $(f - 3)(f + 12)$

25. $(g + 5)(g + 11)$ *26.* $(h - 6)(h + 6)$ *27.* $(j + 12)(j + 10)$

28. $(k - 5)(5 + k)$

29. $(m + 8)(7 + m)$

30. $(n - 6)(10 - n)$

31. $(2v + w)(v - 2w)$

32. $(w + 2x)(w - 3x)$

33. $(3x + 2y)(4x - 5y)$

34. $(2y + 2)(y - 2z)$

35. $(3x + 2y)(2x + 3z)$

36. $(4x - 3z)(2y + 2x)$

3.1 Multiplication of Two Brackets – With Fractions

Worked Examples:

1. $\left(x + \frac{1}{2}\right)\left(x + \frac{1}{2}\right)$

$= x^2 + \frac{1}{2}x + \frac{1}{2}x + \frac{1}{4}$

$= x^2 + x + \frac{1}{4}$

2. $\left(x + \frac{2}{x}\right)\left(x - \frac{1}{x}\right)$

$= x^2 - \frac{x}{x} + \frac{2x}{x} - \frac{2}{x^2}$

$= x^2 - 1 + 2 - \frac{1}{x^2}$

$= x^2 + 1 - \frac{1}{x^2}$

NB: Remember when *multiplying* fractions, multiply the numerators together and denominators together. When *adding* or *subtracting* fractions, a common denominator is needed.

Exercise 3.1

Expand and simplify:

1. $\left(a + \frac{1}{2}\right)(a + 1)$

2. $\left(b - \frac{1}{2}\right)(b + 2)$

3. $\left(c + \frac{1}{2}\right)\left(c - \frac{1}{2}\right)$

4. $\left(d + \frac{1}{3}\right)\left(d + \frac{1}{3}\right)$

5. $\left(e - \frac{2}{3}\right)\left(e - \frac{1}{2}\right)$

6. $\left(f + \frac{1}{4}\right)\left(f - \frac{2}{3}\right)$

7. $\left(g + \frac{3}{4}\right)\left(g + \frac{3}{5}\right)$

8. $\left(h - \frac{1}{5}\right)\left(h - \frac{2}{3}\right)$

9. $\left(j + \frac{1}{4}\right)\left(j - \frac{3}{10}\right)$

10. $\left(2k - \frac{1}{3}\right)\left(k + \frac{1}{8}\right)$

11. $\left(\frac{1}{2}m - \frac{3}{5}\right)\left(3m - \frac{2}{9}\right)$

12. $\left(n - \frac{1}{4}\right)\left(\frac{1}{5}n + \frac{3}{4}\right)$

13. $\left(3p + \frac{3}{4}\right)\left(p + \frac{3}{5}\right)$

14. $\left(2q - \frac{7}{10}\right)\left(q - \frac{1}{4}\right)$

15. $\left(r - \frac{5}{6}\right)\left(2r + \frac{1}{5}\right)$

16. $\left(s - \frac{1}{s}\right)\left(s - \frac{1}{s}\right)$

17. $\left(t - \frac{2}{t}\right)\left(t - \frac{1}{t}\right)$

18. $\left(u - \frac{1}{2u}\right)\left(u + \frac{1}{u}\right)$

19. $\left(v + \frac{3}{v}\right)\left(v + \frac{2}{v}\right)$

20. $\left(\frac{w}{2} - \frac{7}{w}\right)\left(w - \frac{1}{4}\right)$

21. $\left(\frac{2}{x} - x\right)\left(x + \frac{1}{x}\right)$

3.2 Multiplication of Brackets – With Indices

Worked Examples:

1. $x^{\frac{1}{2}}\left(x + x^{\frac{1}{2}}\right)$

$= x^{\frac{3}{2}} + x$

$= \sqrt{x^3} + x$

2. $\left(x + x^{\frac{1}{2}}\right)\left(x + x^{\frac{1}{2}}\right)$

$= x^2 + x^{\frac{3}{2}} + x^{\frac{3}{2}} + x$

$= x^2 + 2x^{\frac{3}{2}} + x$

$= x^2 + 2\sqrt{x^3} + x$

3. $\left(x + x^{\frac{1}{3}}\right)\left(x - x^{-\frac{1}{2}}\right)$

$= x^2 - x^{\frac{1}{2}} + x^{\frac{4}{3}} - x^{-\frac{1}{6}}$

$= x^2 - \sqrt{x} + \sqrt[3]{x^4} - \frac{1}{\sqrt[6]{x}}$

NB: Remember when *multiplying* expressions with indices, the powers are added together.

e.g. $x^{\frac{1}{2}} \times x^{-\frac{3}{2}} = x^{\frac{1}{2} - \frac{3}{2}} = x^{-1} = \frac{1}{x}$

Exercise 3.2

Expand and simplify:

1. $x^2(x^3 + x)$

2. $y^3(y + 1)$

3. $w^2(w^{-1} + w)$

4. $v(v^2 + v^{-1})$

5. $(z - z^2)(z - z^3)$

6. $(u + u^2)(u - u^{-1})$

7. $a^{\frac{1}{2}}\left(a^{\frac{1}{2}} + a\right)$

8. $b^{\frac{1}{2}}\left(b + b^{-\frac{1}{2}}\right)$

9. $c^{\frac{2}{3}}\left(c^{\frac{1}{3}} + c\right)$

10. $d^{\frac{3}{4}}\left(d^{-\frac{1}{4}} + d\right)$

11. $\left(e - e^{\frac{1}{2}}\right)\left(e - e^{\frac{1}{2}}\right)$

12. $\left(f + f^{\frac{1}{2}}\right)\left(f - f^{\frac{1}{2}}\right)$

13. $\left(g + a^{\frac{1}{2}}\right)\left(g + a^{-\frac{1}{2}}\right)$

14. $\left(h - h^{\frac{1}{3}}\right)\left(h - h^{-\frac{1}{3}}\right)$

15. $(j + j^2)\left(j - j^{-\frac{1}{2}}\right)$

16. $\left(k^2 - k^{-\frac{1}{2}}\right)\left(k + k^{-\frac{1}{2}}\right)$

17. $m^{\frac{3}{2}}\left(m - m^{-\frac{1}{2}}\right)$

18. $n^{\frac{3}{2}}(n - \sqrt[3]{n^2})$

19. $\sqrt[3]{p^4}(p - \sqrt{p})$

20. $\sqrt[3]{q}\left(q + \frac{1}{\sqrt{q}}\right)$

21. $\sqrt{r}\left(r^2 + \frac{1}{\sqrt{r}}\right)$

22. $\left(s^{\frac{1}{2}} - s^{-\frac{1}{2}}\right)^2$

23. $\left(t^{\frac{1}{3}} - t^{-\frac{1}{3}}\right)^2$

24. $\left(v^{\frac{2}{3}} - v^{-\frac{2}{3}}\right)^2$

3.3 Multiplication of Brackets – Two by Three

Worked Examples:

1. $(x + 1)(x^2 + 2x + 1)$
$= x^3 + 2x^2 + x + x^2 + 2x + 1$
$= x^3 + 3x^2 + 3x + 1$

2. $(3x - 2)(x^2 + 2x - 5)$
$= 3x^3 + 6x^2 - 15x - 2x^2 - 4x + 10$
$= 3x^3 + 4x^2 - 19x + 10$

NB: When multiplying brackets together, each term in the first bracket must be multiplied by each term in the second bracket.

Exercise 3.3

Expand and simplify:

1. $(a + 1)(a^2 + 2a + 1)$

2. $(b + 2)(b^2 + b + 1)$

3. $(c + 2)(c^2 + 3c + 1)$

4. $(d + 1)(d^2 + 5d + 3)$

5. $(e - 4)(e^2 + 2e + 3)$

6. $(f - 5)(f^2 + 3f - 1)$

7. $(g - 2)(g^2 - 3g + 1)$

8. $(h + 1)(h^2 - 5h - 1)$

9. $(j + 3)(j^2 - 4j + 5)$

10. $(k - 4)(k^2 + 4k - 2)$

11. $(m - 5)(m^2 + 5m + 1)$

12. $(n - 3)(n^2 - n - 4)$

13. $(p + 3)(p^2 + 5p - 1)$

14. $(q + 3)(q^2 - q + 6)$

15. $(r - 3)(r^2 + 4r - 3)$

16. $(s + 3)(2s^2 - 4s + 1)$

17. $(3t + 8)(2t^2 + 5t + 1)$

18. $(3u - 2)(4u^2 + 2u - 1)$

19. $(2v - 2)(v^2 - 5v - 1)$

20. $(w - 3)(4w^2 - 2w + 1)$

21. $(3x + 5)(5x^2 + 3x - 7)$

22. $(2y - 7)(5y^2 + 2y - 9)$

23. $(3z + 8)(5z^2 - 1)$

24. $(5z - 3)(3z^2 - 5)$

3.4 Multiplication of Three Brackets

Worked Examples:

1. $(x + 3)(x - 2)(x + 4)$
$= (x + 3)(x^2 + 2x - 8)$
$= x^3 + 2x^2 - 8x + 3x^2 + 6x - 24$
$= x^3 + 5x^2 - 2x - 24$

2. $(x + 3)^3$
$= (x + 3)(x + 3)(x + 3)$
$= (x + 3)(x^2 + 6x + 9)$
$= x^3 + 6x^2 + 9x + 3x^2 + 18x + 27$
$= x^3 + 9x^2 + 27x + 27$

NB: By expanding the second two brackets, the expression can then be expanded as in Exercise 3.3 (above).

Exercise 3.4

Expand and simplify:

1. $(a + 2)(a + 3)(a + 5)$

2. $(b + 2)(b + 1)(b + 2)$

3. $(c + 4)(c + 1)(c + 6)$

4. $(d + 1)(d - 3)(d - 5)$

5. $(e - 4)(e + 3)(e - 5)$

6. $(f - 5)(f - 1)(f - 3)$

7. $(g - 2)(g + 5)(g - 4)$

8. $(h + 1)(h - 1)(h + 1)$

9. $(j - 3)(j + 5)(j - 7)$

10. $(k - 4)(k - 2)(k - 7)$

11. $(m - 5)(m + 1)(m - 9)$

12. $(n - 3)(n - 4)(n + 9)$

13. $(p - 2)^3$

14. $(q + 3)(q + 6)(q - 3)$

15. $(r - 5)^3$

16. $(s + 4)^3$

17. $(t - 6)^3$

18. $(u - 2)(2u - 1)(u + 3)$

19. $(2v - 2)(v + 1)^2$

20. $(w - 3)^2(w + 1)$

21. $(2x + 5)(x - 7)(2x - 1)$

22. $(2y - 5)(2y - 3)^2$

23. $(3z + 4)^3$

24. $(z - 3)(z^2 - 5)^2$

Chapter 3
Factorising

1.1 Common Factor – Numerical

When factorizing any expression, the first thing to look for is a **common factor**. A common factor is a factor that each of the terms share.

Worked Examples:

1. $5a + 10$
$= 5(a + 2)$

2. $4a + 2b$
$= 2(2a + b)$

3. $12a + 6b - 9c$
$= 3(4a + 2b - 3c)$

Exercise 1.1

Factorise:

1. $3a + 3$

2. $4b - 4$

3. $5c - 15$

4. $6c + 12$

5. $10e - 2$

6. $18f + 9$

7. $6g - 2$

8. $8h - 6$

9. $12i + 15$

10. $18j - 27$

11. $16k - 12$

12. $50m - 10$

13. $12 - 4n$

14. $15 + 10p$

15. $8 - 24q$

16. $24r + 36$

17. $32s - 20$

18. $120t - 45$

19. $6v - 14u$

20. $8w - 32x$

21. $25x + 30y$

22. $45x - 18y + 27z$

23. $32x - 48y + 60z$

24. $100a - 350b + 80c$

1.2 Common Factor – Algebraic

Common factors can also be algebraic terms.

Worked Examples:

1. $5ab + 7a$
$= a(5b + 7)$

2. $4b^2 + 3b$
$= b(4b + 3)$

3. $2a^2b + ab - ab^2$
$= ab(2a + 1 - b)$

Exercise 1.2

Factorise:

1. $3x + 4xb$

2. $4y - yc$

3. $c - 2ct$

4. $5r + 6ar$

5. $10t - 7dt$

6. $3ab + 2bc$

7. $5xy - 3xz$

8. $8abc - 3bcd$

9. $5a^2 - 4a$

10. $v^2 - 7v$

11. $3w^2 + 2wx$

12. $z^2 - 3xz$

13. $5a^2bc - abc$

14. $k^2m - kmn$

15. $c^2d - 2de$

16. $11g^2h - 3eg + 2g$

17. $bcd - 2cd + 3cde$

18. $5v^2wx - vwx^2$

19. $ab^2c + a^2bc$

20. $a^2bc^2 + abc^2$

21. $x^2y^2z + xy^2z - xy^2z^2$

22. $cde^2 + 2cd^2e - c^2d^2e^2$

23. $pqr^2 + 2p^2r - 5p^2qr^2$

24. $st^2 + s^2t - s^2t^2u$

1.3 Common Factor – Numerical and Algebraic

Exercise 1.3

Factorise:

1. $2ab + 6b$

2. $5xy - 15x$

3. $4g + 12gh$

4. $6ac + 8c$

5. $12mn + 15m$

6. $21gr - 12r$

7. $2st - 12tv$

8. $9w^2 + 12w$

9. $5a^2 - 20a$

10. $25n^2 - 10n$

11. $6a^2 + 8a$

12. $30w^2 - 20w$

13. $32a^2 - 24a$

14. $18n^2 - 9n$

15. $3a^2 - 6a$

16. $40d^2 - 12d$

17. $30c + 4c^2$

18. $25bc^2 - 10b^2c$

19. $9ef^2 + 12e^2f$

20. $24y^2 + 8y$

21. $5x^2y^2 + 20xy^2 - 10x^2y$

22. $8de^2 + 12d^2e - 16d^2e^2$

23. $6rst^2 + 2r^2st - 8r^2st^2$

24. $7t^2u + 28tu - 14t^2u^2$

25. $5a^2bc - 20abc$

26. $9m - 27m^2$

27. $32c + 16c^2$

28. $12gh - 18g^2h + 9gh^2$

29. $30c^2de^2 - 2c^2de + 8cde^2$

30. $42gr^2 - 12g^2r$

31. $42a - 30a^2$

32. $14w^2xy^2 + 32wx^2y^2$

33. $28uv + 35uv^2 - 56u^2v$

34. $9de^2 + 12cd^2 - 15c^2d^2e^2$

35. $12cde^2 + 18cd^2e - 15c^2d^2e^2$

36. $8r^2s - 26r^2s^2t + 18rs^2t$

2.1 Difference of Two Squares

A difference of two squares is when one square number is taken away from another, **e.g.** $b^2 - 4$, these may be factorised in the following way:

Worked Examples:

1. $b^2 - a^2$
   $= (b + a)(b - a)$ or
   $= (b - a)(b + a)$

2. $x^2 - 9$
   $= (x + 3)(x - 3)$

3. $25 - y^2$
   $= (5 + y)(5 - y)$

NB: The signs in each bracket are interchangeable (as in example 1), but the terms are not. Example 3 is $(5 + y)(5 - y)$ not $(y + 5)(y - 5)$.

Exercise 2.1

Factorise:

1. $x^2 - y^2$
2. $y^2 - z^2$
3. $a^2 - b^2$
4. $v^2 - u^2$
5. $c^2 - d^2$
6. $m^2 - n^2$
7. $x^2 - 3^2$
8. $x^2 - 5^2$
9. $x^2 - 7^2$
10. $x^2 - 1$
11. $x^2 - 4$
12. $x^2 - 16$
13. $x^2 - 36$
14. $9 - x^2$
15. $x^2 - 64$
16. $1 - x^2$
17. $x^2 - 49$
18. $36 - x^2$
19. $100 - x^2$
20. $x^2 - 81$
21. $x^2 - 144$
22. $x^2 - 169$
23. $121 - x^2$
24. $x^2 - 400$
25. $16 - 9x^2$
26. $4x^2 - 25$
27. $16x^2 - 121$
28. $36x^2 - 169$
29. $1 - 25x^2$
30. $81x^2 - 4$

2.2 Difference of Two Squares with Common Factor

Worked Examples:

1. $2x^2 - 2$
   $= 2(x^2 - 1)$
   $= 2(x + 1)(x - 1)$

2. $4b^2 - 16$
   $= 4(b^2 - 4)$
   $= 4(b + 2)(b - 2)$

NB: When factorising any expression, always take out any common factors first then check if there is anything left to factorise.

Exercise 2.2

Factorise:

1. $5x^2 - 5$
2. $2x^2 - 18$
3. $3x^2 - 12$
4. $5x^2 - 45$
5. $7x^2 - 28$
6. $3x^2 - 27$
7. $10x^2 - 90$
8. $11x^2 - 44$
9. $5x^2 - 125$
10. $\frac{1}{2}x^2 - 2$
11. $\frac{1}{4}x^2 - 9$
12. $4x^2 - 16$
13. $4x^2 - 36$
14. $18 - 2x^2$
15. $\frac{1}{3}x^2 - 3$
16. $100 - 4x^2$
17. $4x^2 - 400$
18. $25x^2 - 100$
19. $400 - 25x^2$
20. $\frac{1}{3}x^2 - 27$
21. $2x^2 - 288$
22. $\frac{1}{5}x^2 - 5$
23. $18 - \frac{1}{2}x^2$
24. $2x^2 - 98$

Trinomials are expressions that consist of three terms written in descending powers of x, **e.g.** $x^2 + 7x + 10$.

When factorising trinomial expressions, consider using the acronym for expanding brackets, **FOIL** (Firsts Outsides Insides Lasts, but in a different order **FLOI**.

Step 1: Start by considering the First terms in the bracket these will be factors of the first term of the trinomial.

Step 1: In the example above, only $x \times x = x^2$
$$x^2 + 7x + 10$$
$$= (x \quad)(x \quad)$$

Step 2: Move to the Last terms in the brackets. These must be factors of the third term in the trinomial.

Step 2:

Factors of 10	Sum
1 and 10	11
2 and 5	7
-1 and -10	-11
-2 and -5	-7

Step 3: The Outsides and Insides of the brackets must add to give the middle term.

Step 3: When the coefficient of x^2 is 1, The sum of the factors of the last term should give the coefficient of the middle term. Therefore, simply add the factors. Only 2 and 5 will result in $+7$.
$$x^2 + 7x + 10$$
$$= (x + 2)(x + 5) \qquad \textbf{Check: } 5x + 2x = 7x \quad \checkmark$$

Worked Examples:

1. $x^2 + 6x + 8$
$= (x + 4)(x + 2)$ **Check:** $2x + 4x = 6x$ ✓

2. $x^2 - 3x - 28$
$= (x - 7)(x + 4)$ **Check:** $4x - 7x = -3x$ ✓

3. $x^2 - 7x + 12$
$= (x - 4)(x - 3)$ **Check:** $-3x - 4x = -7x$ ✓

4. $3x^2 + 4x - 15$
$= (3x - 5)(x + 3)$ **Check:** $9x - 5x = 4x$ ✓

Exercise 2.3

Factorise:

1. $x^2 + 2x + 1$

2. $x^2 + 4x + 3$

3. $x^2 + 3x + 2$

4. $x^2 + 5x + 6$

5. $x^2 + 5x + 4$

6. $x^2 + 4x + 4$

7. $x^2 + 7x + 10$

8. $x^2 + 7x + 6$

9. $x^2 + 6x + 8$

10. $x^2 + 10x + 9$

11. $x^2 + 9x + 8$

12. $x^2 + 6x + 9$

13. $x^2 + 8x + 15$

14. $x^2 + 7x + 12$

15. $x^2 + 8x + 12$

16. $x^2 + 16x + 15$

17. $x^2 + 12x + 20$

18. $x^2 + 13x + 12$

19. $x^2 + 10x + 24$

20. $x^2 + 12x + 36$

21. $x^2 + 11x + 24$

22. $x^2 + 25x + 100$

23. $x^2 + 10x + 25$

24. $x^2 + 17x + 30$

2.4 Trinomials – Both Brackets Negative

When the **last term** in a trinomial expression is positive, the signs in the brackets must be *the same*. If the **middle term** is negative, both the signs in the brackets will be negative.

Worked Example:

$$x^2 - 6x + 8 = (x - 4)(x - 2)$$

Negative   Positive   Both Negative

Exercise 2.4

Factorise:

1. $x^2 - 2x + 1$

2. $x^2 - 4x + 3$

3. $x^2 - 5x + 4$

4. $x^2 - 7x + 6$

5. $x^2 - 4x + 4$

6. $x^2 - 7x + 12$

7. $x^2 - 11x + 10$

8. $x^2 - 8x + 12$

9. $x^2 - 8x + 15$

10. $x^2 - 10x + 24$

11. $x^2 - 12x + 32$

12. $x^2 - 16x + 28$

13. $x^2 - 14x + 24$

14. $x^2 - 14x + 24$

15. $x^2 - 10x + 25$

16. $x^2 - 12x + 27$

17. $x^2 - 9x + 20$

18. $x^2 - 21x + 20$

19. $x^2 - 22x + 40$

20. $x^2 - 18x + 32$

21. $x^2 - 13x + 42$

22. $x^2 - 20x + 64$

23. $x^2 - 11x + 30$

24. $x^2 - 21x + 80$

2.5 Trinomials – One Bracket Negative

When the **last term** in a trinomial expression is *negative*, the signs in the brackets must be *different*.

Worked Example:

$$x^2 - 2x - 8 = (x - 4)(x + 2)$$

Negative   Different signs

For simple trinomials with an x^2 coefficient of 1; if the **middle term** is negative, the bracket with the larger term will be negative. In the same way, if the **middle term** is positive, the bracket with the larger term will be positive.

Exercise 2.5

Factorise:

1. $x^2 - x - 2$

2. $x^2 + 2x - 3$

3. $x^2 - 3x - 4$

4. $x^2 - 5x - 6$

5. $x^2 + 2x - 8$

6. $x^2 + x - 12$

7. $x^2 - 4x - 12$

8. $x^2 - 10x - 24$

9. $x^2 + 6x - 16$

10. $x^2 - 11x - 12$	11. $x^2 + x - 2$	12. $x^2 + 2x - 24$
13. $x^2 + 4x - 5$	14. $x^2 + 5x - 36$	15. $x^2 + 2x - 15$
16. $x^2 - x - 20$	17. $x^2 + 9x - 10$	18. $x^2 + 5x - 24$
19. $x^2 - 3x - 40$	20. $x^2 - 21x - 100$	21. $x^2 - 9x - 36$
22. $x^2 + 12x - 45$	23. $x^2 + 7x - 30$	24. $x^2 - 12x - 64$
25. $12 - x - x^2$	26. $15 + 2x - x^2$	27. $8 - 7x - x^2$
28. $24 + 5x - x^2$	29. $36 - 5x - x^2$	30. $120 + 14x - x^2$

2.6 Trinomials – Mixed Exercise

Exercise 2.6

Factorise:

1. $x^2 + 5x + 6$	2. $x^2 - 8x - 9$	3. $x^2 + 5x - 14$
4. $x^2 - 8x + 12$	5. $x^2 - 11x + 24$	6. $x^2 - 5x - 36$
7. $x^2 - 9x + 18$	8. $x^2 - 13x + 42$	9. $x^2 - 8x + 16$
10. $x^2 + x - 30$	11. $x^2 - 6x - 16$	12. $x^2 - 10x + 24$
13. $x^2 - x - 56$	14. $x^2 + 15x + 36$	15. $x^2 - 4x - 12$
16. $x^2 + 13x - 14$	17. $x^2 + 12x + 32$	18. $x^2 + 48x - 100$
19. $x^2 - 10x - 24$	20. $x^2 + x - 42$	21. $x^2 + 18x + 81$
22. $x^2 - 20x + 64$	23. $x^2 - 17x - 200$	24. $x^2 - 14x + 45$
25. $x^2 - 2x - 48$	26. $x^2 + 11x - 80$	27. $x^2 + 19x + 78$
28. $x^2 - 7x - 60$	29. $x^2 + x - 72$	30. $x^2 - 13x - 30$

2.7 Trinomials – Non-unitary Coefficient of x^2

For trinomials with a coefficient of x^2 greater than 1, follow the instruction set out in **section 2.3**. Until confident, trial and error with factors can be the quickest method.

Worked Examples:

1. $2x^2 - x - 6$
   $= (2x + 3)(x - 2)$ **Check:** $-4x + 3x = -x$ ✓

2. $6x^2 + 5x - 4$
   $= \cancel{(6x - 1)(x + 4)}$ **Check:** $24x - x = 23x$ ✗
   $= \cancel{(3x - 1)(2x + 4)}$ **Check:** $12x - 2x = 10x$ ✗
   $= (3x + 4)(2x - 1)$ **Check:** $-3x + 8x = 5x$ ✓

Exercise 2.7

Factorise:

1. $2x^2 + 7x + 3$
2. $3x^2 - 13x + 4$
3. $5x^2 - 14x - 3$
4. $2x^2 - 7x + 6$
5. $2x^2 - x - 15$
6. $3x^2 + 7x - 6$
7. $2x^2 - 3x - 2$
8. $5x^2 + 3x - 2$
9. $3x^2 - 11x - 4$
10. $2x^2 + 11x + 5$
11. $3x^2 + 5x - 2$
12. $5x^2 - 13x + 6$
13. $4x^2 + 27x - 7$
14. $5x^2 - x - 4$
15. $3x^2 - 8x + 5$
16. $4x^2 + 16x + 7$
17. $6x^2 - 31x + 5$
18. $8x^2 + 11x + 3$
19. $7x^2 + 19x - 6$
20. $6x^2 + 5x - 21$
21. $4x^2 - 13x - 12$
22. $5x^2 + 3x - 14$
23. $4x^2 - 12x - 27$
24. $6x^2 + 25x + 25$
25. $4x^2 - 4x - 35$
26. $8x^2 - 35x - 25$
27. $12x^2 + x - 6$
28. $6x^2 + 5x - 14$
29. $12x^2 - 8x - 15$
30. $12x^2 - 23x - 24$

2.8 Factorising – Mixed Exercises

Exercise 2.8A

Fully factorise:

1. $3x^2 + 6x$
2. $x^2 - 4x$
3. $3x^2 - 3$
4. $x^2 - 4x - 12$
5. $2x^2 - 8x - 10$
6. $x^2 + 7x + 12$
7. $x^2 - 9$
8. $10x^2 + 10x$
9. $x^2 + 2x + 1$
10. $9x^2 + 63x$
11. $3x^2 - 12$
12. $x^2 - 11x + 10$
13. $64 - 4x^2$
14. $18 - 3x - x^2$
15. $x^2 + 13x + 12$
16. $7x^2y + 14xy$
17. $2x^2 - 16x - 40$
18. $27 - 3x^2$
19. $12x^3yz + 18xy$
20. $3x^2 - 4x - 6$
21. $12x - 12x^3$
22. $4x^2 - 16x + 16$
23. $45 + 6x - 3x^2$
24. $3x^4 - 3$

Exercise 2.8B

Fully factorise:

1. $2x^2 + 8x$
2. $x^2 - 16x$
3. $3x^2 - 27$

4. $x^2 - 9x + 8$

5. $2x^2 - 4x - 6$

6. $3x^2 + 7x - 6$

7. $x^2 - 1$

8. $5x^2 + 10x$

9. $3x^2 + 2x - 5$

10. $24x^2 + 60x$

11. $x^2 + 4x - 12$

12. $4x^2 - 28x + 40$

13. $100 - 4x^2$

14. $8 - 2x - x^2$

15. $7x^2 + 8x - 12$

16. $4x^2y^2 + 16xy^2 + 12xy$

17. $4x^2 - 14x + 6$

18. $128 - 2x^2$

19. $5x^3 - 125x$

20. $x^2 - 15x + 54$

21. $48x - 12x^3$

22. $4x^2 - 12x - 27$

23. $18 + 3x - x^2$

24. $30 - 13x - 3x^2$

3.1 Factorising Polynomials

A polynomial is an expression with multiple terms of decreasing positive powers of x, these are usually considered to be expressions with a power higher than 2, such as $x^3 - 3x + 2$.

Polynomials can be factorized using **synthetic division**.

Worked Example:

Factorise $x^3 - 3x + 2$

Step 1: Set up synthetic division using coefficients from polynomial in decreasing powers of x. For the example $x^3 - 3x + 2$, the coefficients are $1, 0, -3$ and 2. If there is no term (in this case, no x^2) the coefficient is 0.

Step 2: The value outside of the division is derived from factors of the last term (in the example above, factors of 2)

Step 3: Add each number vertically, then multiply by the value outside of the division. If the remainder of the division is 0 then the value outside the division is a root and from this the factor may be derived, **e.g.** if -3 is a root, $(x + 3)$ is a factor.

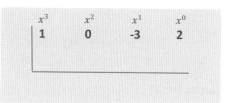

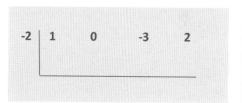

$\therefore x^3 - 3x + 2$
$= (x + 2)(x^2 - 2x + 1)$
$= (x + 2)(x - 1)(x - 1)$

NB: The remaining values under the line are the coefficients of the quotient.

Step 4: If the quotient is not a quadratic, repeat the process with the quotient until a quadratic, then factorise as usual (as in the solution above).

Exercise 3.1

Fully factorise:

1. $x^3 + 2x^2 - x - 2$

2. $x^3 + 4x^2 - 4x - 16$

3. $x^3 + x^2 - 5x + 3$

4. $x^3 - 4x^2 + x + 6$

5. $x^4 - 1$

6. $x^3 - 2x^2 - 13x - 10$

7. $x^3 - 5x^2 + 7x - 3$

8. $x^3 + 5x^2 + 2x - 8$

9. $x^4 - 16$

10. $x^3 - x^2 - 22x + 40$

11. $x^3 - 3x^2 + 3x - 1$

12. $2x^3 + x^2 - 13x + 6$

13. $x^3 + 6x^2 + 11x + 6$

14. $x^3 - x^2 - 22x + 40$

15. $x^4 - 4x^3 + 16x - 16$

16. $x^4 - 8x^2 - 9$

17. $x^4 + 2x^2 - 3$

18. $x^3 + 4x^2 + x - 6$

19. $x^3 - 2x^2 - 13x - 10$

20. $x^4 - 5x^3 + 9x^2 - 7x + 2$

21. $x^4 + 2x^3 - 15x^2 + 4x + 20$

22. $2x^3 + 7x^2 + 7x + 2$

23. $x^3 + 4x^2 - 9x - 36$

24. $x^4 + 2x^3 - 3x^2 - 4x + 4$

25. $x^3 + x^2 - 4x - 4$

26. $x^3 + 5x^2 + 3x - 9$

27. $x^4 - 6x^3 + 8x^2 + 6x - 9$

Chapter 4
Solving Equations 1 – Linear Equations

1.1 Solving Equations: $x + a = b$

To solve an equation, is to find the unknown value which makes the equation true.

For example, if $x + 1 = 3$, then the only value that x can be is 2, as $2 + 1 = 3$. So the solution is $x = 2$.

There are many methods to solve equations, but this book will consider only the **balancing method**. In the balancing method, an equation is treated like an old-fashioned balance. In order to keep the balance equal and balanced, then it is necessary to add or subtract *the same amount to both sides of the balance*. It is the same with equations.

Worked Examples:

1. $x + 4 = 5$
   $(-4) \quad (-4)$
   $x = 1$

2. $y - 7 = 10$
   $(+7) \quad (+7)$
   $y = 17$

3. $z + 6 = 2$
   $(-6) \quad (-6)$
   $z = -4$

Exercise 1.1A

Solve the following equations:

1. $a + 4 = 6$
2. $b + 3 = 11$
3. $c + 3 = 5$
4. $8 + d = 9$

5. $e + 6 = 22$
6. $3 + f = 5$
7. $g + 2 = 7$
8. $h + 4 = 5$

9. $i + 10 = 30$
10. $18 = j + 3$
11. $k + 9 = 10$
12. $l + 5 = 22$

13. $m + 5 = 10$
14. $n + 2 = 35$
15. $4 + p = 19$
16. $38 = q + 5$

17. $r + 14 = 61$
18. $15 + s = 16$
19. $17 = 13 + t$
20. $u + 5 = 11$

21. $v + 17 = 18$
22. $w + 18 = 19$
23. $19 = x + 13$
24. $y + 22 = 22$

25. $z + 29 = 54$
26. $42 = 37 + a$
27. $c + 17 = 59$
28. $w + 29 = 41$

29. $r + 6 = 11$
30. $t + 1 = 0$
31. $z + 2 = 0$
32. $a + 9 = 2$

33. $c + 15 = 5$
34. $x + 14 = 9$
35. $y + 5 = -3$
36. $u + 7 = -3$

37. $t + 11 = 4$
38. $w + 5 = -11$
39. $z + 6 = -9$
40. $b + 3 = -1$

Exercise 1.1B

Solve the following equations:

1. $a - 4 = 8$
2. $b - 5 = 11$
3. $c - 3 = 10$
4. $d - 8 = 9$

5. $e - 6 = 12$
6. $f - 3 = 1$
7. $g - 2 = 7$
8. $h - 4 = 5$

9. $i - 10 = 30$
10. $18 = j - 3$
11. $k - 9 = 10$
12. $l - 5 = 15$

13. $m - 5 = 4$
14. $n - 2 = 16$
15. $p - 4 = 12$
16. $q - 5 = 22$

17. $r - 14 = 52$

18. $s - 15 = 16$

19. $t - 13 = 1$

20. $u - 5 = 0$

21. $v - 17 = 18$

22. $w - 18 = 19$

23. $x - 13 = 17$

24. $y - 22 = 32$

25. $z - 29 = 54$

26. $21 = a - 37$

27. $c - 17 = 6$

28. $w - 29 = 1$

29. $r - 3 = 11$

30. $t - 1 = 0$

31. $z - 2 = 0$

32. $2 = a - 9$

33. $c - 1 = -2$

34. $x - 14 = 9$

35. $y - 1 = -3$

36. $u - 3 = -3$

37. $t - 11 = -14$

38. $w - 5 = -11$

39. $z - 6 = -9$

40. $b - 3 = -10$

1.2 Solving Equations: $ax = b$

When solving equations of the form $ax = b$, always divide by the coefficient of the algebraic term.

Worked Examples:

1. $2x = 6$

$(\div 2)\quad(\div 2)$

$x = 3$

2. $8y = -24$

$(\div 8)\quad(\div 8)$

$y = -3$

3. $\dfrac{z}{3} = 2$

$(\times 3)\quad(\times 3)$

$z = 6$

Exercise 1.2A

Solve the following equations:

1. $4a = 12$

2. $2b = 8$

3. $5c = 5$

4. $6d = 18$

5. $3e = 9$

6. $7f = 28$

7. $4g = 20$

8. $10h = 50$

9. $6i = 24$

10. $5j = 40$

11. $9k = 36$

12. $7l = 35$

13. $5m = 25$

14. $8n = 32$

15. $12p = 60$

16. $20q = 100$

17. $15r = 30$

18. $11s = 55$

19. $6t = 6$

20. $12u = 24$

21. $9v = -18$

22. $2w = -6$

23. $6x = -36$

24. $10y = -200$

25. $7z = 42$

26. $20a = -400$

27. $10y = 5$

28. $6t = 30$

29. $8r = -56$

30. $4t = 0$

31. $8m = -24$

32. $30g = 600$

33. $8d = 4$

34. $6c = -3$

35. $4y = -20$

36. $24v = 12$

37. $6t = 126$

38. $3x = 1$

39. $4z = -1$

40. $10p = -5$

Exercise 1.2B

Solve the following equations:

1. $\dfrac{a}{2} = 3$

2. $\dfrac{b}{2} = 5$

3. $\dfrac{c}{3} = 3$

4. $\dfrac{d}{4} = 2$

5. $\dfrac{e}{2} = 6$

6. $\dfrac{f}{5} = 4$

7. $\dfrac{g}{4} = 6$

8. $\dfrac{1}{2}h = 5$

9. $\dfrac{1}{3}i = 7$

10. $\dfrac{1}{4}j = 2$

11. $\dfrac{1}{5}k = -2$

12. $\dfrac{1}{2}l = -5$

13. $\dfrac{m}{4} = -6$

14. $\dfrac{1}{5}n = -1$

15. $\dfrac{p}{3} = -5$

16. $\dfrac{1}{3}q = -6$

17. $\dfrac{2}{3}r = 4$

18. $\dfrac{3}{4}s = 6$

19. $\dfrac{2t}{3} = 4$

20. $\dfrac{3u}{2} = 9$

1.3 Solving Equations: $ax + b = c$

When solving equations of the form $ax + b = c$, add or subtract, then divide or multiply.

Worked Examples:

1. $2x - 5 = 11$
   $(+5) \quad (+5)$
   $2x = 16$
   $(\div 2) \quad (\div 2)$
   $x = 8$

2. $5y + 16 = 1$
   $(-16) \quad (-16)$
   $5y = -15$
   $(\div 5) \quad (\div 5)$
   $y = -3$

3. $\dfrac{1}{2}z + 3 = 4$
   $(-3) \quad (-3)$
   $\dfrac{1}{2}z = 1$
   $(\times 2) \quad (\times 2)$
   $z = 2$

4. $15 - 2x = 9$
   $(-15) \quad (-15)$
   $-2x = -6$
   $(\div -2) \quad (\div -2)$
   $x = 3$

NB: It is good practice to keep the equals signs lined up as in the examples above.

Exercise 1.3

Solve the following equations:

1. $2a + 4 = 8$

2. $4b - 6 = 14$

3. $3c + 3 = 21$

4. $5d - 4 = 41$

5. $2e - 5 = 11$

6. $6f - 1 = 35$

7. $3g + 5 = 26$

8. $9h - 10 = 17$

9. $5i - 3 = 22$

10. $4j + 7 = 31$

11. $3k + 15 = 24$

12. $5l + 5 = 5$

13. $6m + 18 = 24$

14. $7n + 12 = 5$

15. $5p + 11 = 1$

16. $6q + 28 = 4$

17. $\dfrac{1}{2}r - 3 = 6$

18. $5s + 10 = 0$

19. $4t + 20 = 8$

20. $7u - 16 = 26$

21. $\dfrac{1}{2}v - 5 = 3$

22. $2w + 1 = 1$

23. $\dfrac{1}{2}x + 6 = 10$

24. $10 - y = 20$

25. $14 - z = 4$

26. $4 - 2a = 8$

27. $\frac{1}{2}y + 6 = 3$

28. $6t + 5 = 35$

29. $15 + 2t = 41$

30. $40 + 3t = 1$

31. $12 - 3m = -24$

32. $\frac{1}{2}g + 4 = 28$

33. $8d + 6 = 10$

34. $5 - 4c = -3$

35. $3 + \frac{1}{2}y = 4$

36. $15v + 28 = -2$

37. $5t - 4 = 46$

38. $3 - 2x = 1$

39. $7 - 3z = -2$

40. $5 - \frac{1}{2}p = 5$

1.4 Numbers and Letters on Both Sides

When solving equations of the form $ax + b = cx + d$, add or subtract the algebraic term first.

Worked Examples:

1. $4x + 4 = 2x + 6$
   $(-2x) \quad (-2x)$
   $2x + 4 = 6$
   $(-4) \quad (-4)$
   $2x = 2$
   $(\div 2) \quad (\div 2)$
   $x = 1$

2. $8 + 6y = 40 - 2y$
   $(+2y) \quad (+2y)$
   $8 + 8y = 40$
   $(-8) \quad (-8)$
   $8y = 32$
   $(\div 8) \quad (\div 8)$
   $y = 4$

3. $2z + 12 = 5z + 3$
   $(-2z) \quad (-2z)$
   $12 = 3z + 3$
   $(-3) \quad (-3)$
   $9 = 3z$
   $(\div 3) \quad (\div 3)$
   $3 = z$
   $z = 3$

NB: To avoid dividing by a negative number, determine which side will give you a positive value of the algebraic term (sometimes this will be the right-hand side, as in example 3).

Exercise 1.4

Solve the following equations:

1. $4a + 2 = 2a + 8$

2. $7b - 3 = 2b + 7$

3. $3c - 6 = 2c + 5$

4. $10d - 4 = 6d + 20$

5. $5e + 5 = 2e + 26$

6. $4f + 3 = 2f + 11$

7. $3g - 8 = 2g - 5$

8. $4h - 4 = h + 14$

9. $7i + 8 = 4i + 23$

10. $6j + 5 = 4j + 21$

11. $3k + 15 = 39 - k$

12. $5l + 12 = 2l - 12$

13. $8m - 8 = 5m - 2$

14. $10n - 12 = 2n - 4$

15. $5p + 11 = 8p - 4$

16. $6q - 8 = 4q - 10$

17. $6 - 3r = 5r - 10$

18. $6s + 20 = 2s - 16$

19. $3t + 25 = 6t + 7$

20. $5u - 16 = 2u + 17$

21. $4 - 2v = 3v + 34$

22. $8w + 12 = 2w + 6$

23. $4x + 24 = x - 12$

24. $18 - 4y = y - 2$

25. $23 - 6z = z - 5$

26. $32 - 3b = 6b - 4$

27. $3t + 6 = 7t - 18$

28. $9t + 5 = 15t + 47$

29. $6c + 4 = 18 - c$

30. $35 + 11r = 9 - 2r$

31. $24 - m = 5m + 24$

32. $7 - g = 28 + 6g$

33. $2h + 6 = 6h - 34$

34. $5d - 10 = d - 6$

35. $10y - 5 = 13y + 10$

36. $15 - 6v = 20 - 7v$

1.5 Equations with Rational Solutions

A **rational number** is any number that can be expressed as a division of two integers, or more simply, a number that can be expressed as a fraction.

Worked Examples:

1. $7x = 2$

$(\div 7) \quad (\div 7)$

$x = \frac{2}{7}$

2. $4x + 4 = 7$

$(-4) \quad (-4)$

$4x = 3$

$(\div 4) \quad (\div 4)$

$x = \frac{3}{4}$

3. $6z + 10 = 3z + 3$

$(-3z) \quad (-3z)$

$3z + 10 = 3$

$(-10) \quad (-10)$

$3z = -7$

$(\div 3) \quad (\div 3)$

$z = \frac{-7}{3}$

Exercise 1.5

Solve the following equations:

1. $4a = 11$

2. $6b + 3 = 7$

3. $5c + 8 = c + 5$

4. $5d - 4 = 20$

5. $9e = -15$

6. $7f + 2 = 3f - 5$

7. $6g - 7 = 2g - 5$

8. $3h - 5 = h + 14$

9. $8i - 3 = 5i - 10$

10. $6j + 8 = 3j - 21$

11. $11k - 15 = k + 6$

12. $5l + 9 = 2l - 4$

13. $4m - 6 = 8m - 4$

14. $6n = 2n - 5$

15. $5p + 1 = 7p + 2$

16. $q - 8 = 3q - 5$

17. $5 - 2r = 6r - 9$

18. $3s + 15 = 5s - 2$

19. $6 - 3t = 4$

20. $7 - 3u = 3u - 7$

21. $9 - 3v = 1$

22. $18 = 3 - 2w$

23. $5 - 7x = 0$

24. $1 = 18 - 4y$

25. $x = 4 - 3x$

26. $7b = 1 + 12b$

27. $6u = 1 - 7u$

28. $5 = 8 - 2r$

29. $15 + 4x = 0$

30. $6 = 25 - 5y$

1.6 Equations with Brackets

When solving equations with brackets, first expand the brackets and simiplify, then solve the equations as above. (For further practice on expanding brackets, see **chapter 2, exercises 1.1-1.3**)

Worked Examples:

1. $3(x + 2) = 12$
   $3x + 6 = 12$
   $3x = 6$
   $x = 2$

2. $5(y + 3) = 2(y - 1)$
   $5y + 15 = 2y - 2$
   $3y + 15 = -2$
   $3y = -17$
   $y = \frac{-17}{3}$

3. $4(z + 2) - 2(z - 3) = 5z + 1$
   $4z + 8 - 2z + 6 = 5z + 1$
   $2z + 14 = 5z + 1$
   $14 = 3z + 1$
   $13 = 3z$
   $z = \frac{13}{3}$

Exercise 1.6A

Solve the following equations:

1. $5(a + 2) = 15$
2. $6(b - 1) = 24$
3. $4(c - 2) = 28$

4. $3(d + 6) = 9$
5. $5(e + 5) = 5$
6. $7(f + 2) = 14$

7. $3(g - 8) = 3$
8. $2(h - 4) = h + 4$
9. $6(i + 2) = 2i + 5$

10. $4(j + 1) = 3j + 15$
11. $5(k + 2) = k + 6$
12. $5(l + 1) = 3l - 5$

13. $9(m - 2) = 5(m - 2)$
14. $6(n + 3) = 2(n - 2)$
15. $5(p + 1) = 2(p - 4)$

16. $6(q - 5) = 3(q - 2)$
17. $2(r + 4) = 5(r - 2)$
18. $5(s + 4) = 3s - 16$

19. $3(t + 5) = 7(t + 7)$
20. $8(u - 2) = 3(u + 5)$
21. $7(v + 9) = 3(v + 4)$

22. $4(5 - w) = 3(w + 7)$
23. $7(3 - 2x) = 2(4 - x)$
24. $5(3 - y) = 5(3y + 1)$

Exercise 1.6B

Solve the following equations:

1. $4(m + 2) - 5 = 5(2m - 3)$
2. $10(g - 2) - 3(g + 5) = 6g$

3. $3(h + 3) - (4 - h) = 6h - 5$
4. $8(d - 6) + 2(d + 9) = 4(d - 7)$

5. $10(y - 2) - (y - 3) = 5(y + 3)$
6. $5(2 - v) - (4 - 7v) = 6 - 3v$

7. $3(r + 7) - 5(4 - r) = 5(r - 5)$
8. $6(t - 4) + 4(5 - t) = 4(6 - t)$

9. $8(z - 9) - (5 - z) = 4(z + 3)$
10. $7(3 - x) - (8 - 6x) = 6 - 5x$

11. $5 = 2 - 2(a - 5)$
12. $6(b - 4) = 5 - 4(6 - b)$

13. $y - 15 = 17 - 3(y - 3)$
14. $6 - (5 - 3x) = 4 - (6 - 7x)$

1.7 Forming Equations

Many real-life problems involving number can be solved by forming and solving equations.

Worked Examples:

1. Seven bananas cost 84 pence. By forming an equation, find how much one banana costs.

$$7b = 84$$
$$b = 12$$

∴ One banana costs 12 pence.

2. David is paid £d per hour, Fiona is paid twice as much. Zahid earns, £3 more per hour than David. Altogether in 1 hour, they earn £35. How much does David earn per hour?

$$d + 2d + (d + 3) = 35$$
$$4d + 3 = 35$$
$$4d = 32$$
$$d = 8$$

∴ David earns £8 per hour.

3. The perimeter of the rectangle is 44cm. Find the length and breadth.

$(x - 4)$cm

$(2x + 2)$cm

$$2(2x + 2) + 2(x - 4) = 44$$
$$4x + 4 + 2x - 8 = 44$$
$$6x - 4 = 44$$
$$6x = 48$$
$$x = 8$$

∴ Length = $2 \times 8 + 2 = 18$cm

Breadth = $8 - 4 = 4$cm

Exercise 1.7

<u>By forming an equation</u>, solve the following problems:

1. Five apples cost £1.20. How much does one apple cost?

2. Eight peaches cost £2. How much does 1 peach cost?

3. Six litres of fuel cost £7.80. How much does one litre cost?

4. Twelve cans of juice cost £6.60. How much does each can cost?

5. Saima runs 8 kilometers in 36 minutes. How long does she take to run 1 kilometre?

6. Michael weighs 81kg. He is three times as heavy as his younger sister. What does his sister weigh?

7. Jamelia is 3kg heavier than Mo, together they weigh 79kg. How much does Mo weigh?

8. Peter goes for a walk on Monday and Tuesday. He walks three times as far on Tuesday than Monday. Altogether he walks 28km. How far does he walk on Monday?

9. Karen exercises for three days one week. On Tuesday she exercises for twice as long as Monday. On Wednesday she exercises for five minutes more than Tuesday. Altogether she exercises for 80 minutes. How long does she exercise on Monday?

10. A dealer buys three cars, one red, one blue and one silver. The blue car costs four times the red car, the silver car costs £3000 more than the red car. Together they cost £21,000. How much does the blue car cost?

11. Lucas has homework for Maths, English and French. He spends twice as long on Maths than he does on English and 10 minutes less on French than English. He spends 50 minutes on his homework. How long does he spend on French?

12. Alexa cycles three days in one week. On the second day she cycles three times as far as the first day. On the third day she cycles 12km less than the first day. Altogether she cycles 78km. How far does she cycle on the second day?

13. Three puppies weigh 5200g. Fido is 400g heavier than Jess. Jess is 600g lighter than Sheba. How heavy is Sheba?

14. Cameron has homework for Physics, Chemistry and Biology. He spends half as long on Physics than he does on Chemistry and 15 minutes less on Chemistry than Biology. He spends two hours on his homework. How long does he spend on Physics?

15. Three runners run a relay race, the first runner is 6 seconds quicker than the second, the second runner is 4 seconds slower than the third runner. They finish in 2 minutes and 11 seconds. How fast is the first runner?

16. Three kittens weigh 1900g. Puss is 100g heavier than Thomson. Thomson is 300g lighter than Garfield. How heavy is Thomson?

17. Three antiques cost £39,000. The painting costs five times the cost of the vase, clock costs £5000 less than the painting. How much does the vase cost?

In the following questions, form an equation to find the unknown value:

18. Perimeter = 22cm

$(x - 1)$cm

$(x + 2)$cm

19. Perimeter = 32cm

$(x - 3)$cm

$(x + 5)$cm

20. Perimeter = 44cm

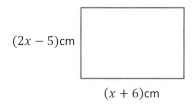

$(2x - 5)$cm

$(x + 6)$cm

21. Perimeter = 28cm

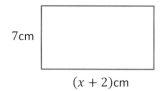

$(3x - 9)$cm

$(2x + 3)$cm

22. Area = 15cm²

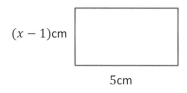

$(x - 1)$cm

5cm

23. Area = 56cm²

7cm

$(x + 2)$cm

24. Area = 117cm²

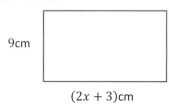

9cm

$(2x + 3)$cm

25. Area = 84cm²

$(3x - 9)$cm

14cm

1.8 Solving Basic Inequations

An **inequation** or **inequality** is a statement that a value lies within a certain range of values. For example, the statement $x < 7$ means that x is less than 7. Therefore, x could be 6, 5, 4, 0.5, -200, or indeed any number, so long as it is less than 7. For most purposes, to state that $x < 7$ is sufficient.

Inequations are solved *in the same way as equations*, with two exceptions. Firstly, if multiplying or dividing by a negative value, the inequality sign is reversed (example 3). Secondly, when the unknown is on the right of the inequality, the sign must be reversed to move the unknown to the left (example 4).

Inequality Symbols

$>$ means "is greater than"
$\geq$ means "is greater than or equal to"
$<$ means "is less than"
$\leq$ means "is less than or equal to"

Worked Examples:

1. $5x > 2$
   $(\div 5) \quad (\div 5)$
   $x > \frac{2}{5}$

2. $3x + 4 \leq 7$
   $(-4) \quad (-4)$
   $3x \leq 3$
   $(\div 3) \quad (\div 3)$
   $x \leq 1$

3. $2z + 10 \geq 3z + 22$
   $(-3z) \quad (-3z)$
   $-z + 10 \geq 22$
   $(-10) \quad (-10)$
   $-z \geq 12$
   $(\div -1) \quad (\div -1)$
   $z \leq -12$

4. $3y + 5 \geq 7y + 2$
   $(-3y) \quad (-3y)$
   $5 \geq 4y + 2$
   $(-5) \quad (-5)$
   $3 \geq 4y$
   $(\div 4) \quad (\div 4)$
   $\frac{3}{4} \geq y$
   $y \leq \frac{3}{4}$

NB: To avoid dividing by a negative number, determine which side will give you a positive value of the algebraic term (sometimes this will be the right-hand side, as in example 3).

Exercise 1.8A

Solve the following inequations:

1. $4a > 12$
2. $2b < 10$
3. $5c \geq 20$
4. $6d > 12$
5. $3e \geq 15$
6. $7f \leq 42$
7. $4g > 16$
8. $10h \leq 70$
9. $6i > 36$
10. $5j < 35$
11. $9k \geq 54$
12. $7l < 49$
13. $5m \leq 75$
14. $8n > 56$
15. $12p < 72$
16. $15q \geq 60$
17. $17r < 51$
18. $11s \leq 44$
19. $6t > 0$
20. $12u < 36$

Exercise 1.8B

Solve the following inequations:

1. $a + 3 > 9$
2. $b - 4 \leq 12$
3. $c + 2 < 7$
4. $d - 9 \geq 9$
5. $e - 1 \leq 2$
6. $f + 3 > 2$
7. $g + 8 \geq 7$
8. $h - 6 < 5$
9. $i + 11 \geq 5$
10. $5 < j - 2$
11. $k + 9 \leq 2$
12. $2 > 15 - L$
13. $5 \geq 4 + m$
14. $n + 12 > 16$
15. $4 - p < 6$
16. $7 - q \leq 2$
17. $4 > 5 + r$
18. $7 \leq 6 - s$
19. $t - 3 < -3$
20. $0 \geq 5 - u$

Exercise 1.8C

Solve the following inequations:

1. $2a + 2 < 6$
2. $4b - 4 > 12$
3. $3c + 3 \geq 30$
4. $5d - 4 \leq 26$
5. $2e - 7 > 11$
6. $6f - 2 \leq 10$
7. $3g + 5 < 2$
8. $9h - 8 \geq 19$
9. $5i + 3 \leq 28$
10. $4j + 12 \geq 8$
11. $3k + 20 > 2$
12. $5 < 5 - 2l$
13. $18 - 6m \geq 24$
14. $12 < 5 - 7n$
15. $11 \leq 1 - 5p$
16. $28 - 6q > 4$
17. $3 < 6 - \frac{1}{2}r$
18. $\frac{1}{4}s + 6 \geq 0$
19. $0 > 8 - 4t$
20. $1 \leq 2 - \frac{1}{3}u$

Exercise 1.8D

Solve the following inequations:

1. $6a + 4 < 2a + 8$
2. $4b - 3 \leq 2b + 11$
3. $5c - 6 > 2c + 6$
4. $8d - 4 \geq 6d + 10$
5. $9e + 5 > 2e + 33$
6. $10f + 3 < 2f + 11$
7. $3g - 7 \leq g + 5$
8. $h - 4 < 2h + 14$
9. $5i + 8 \leq 4i + 23$

10. $6j + 5 < 7j + 11$ 11. $k + 15 \leq 9 - 5k$ 12. $2l + 12 > 5l - 3$

13. $8 - 3m \geq 5m - 16$ 14. $13 - 3n > 4 - 6n$ 15. $3p + 12 \geq 11p - 4$

16. $8 - 5q > 3q - 24$ 17. $6 - 3r \leq 9r - 30$ 18. $20 + s < 2 - 5s$

2.1 Equations with Fractions

To solve equations involving fractions, multiply everything by the *denominator* of the fraction.

Worked Examples:

1. $\dfrac{x}{4} = 5$
$(\times 4)\quad(\times 4)$
$x = 20$

2. $\dfrac{2x}{3} = 8$
$(\times 3)\quad(\times 3)$
$2x = 24$
$(\div 2)\quad(\div 2)$
$x = 12$

3. $\dfrac{2}{5}x = 3$
$(\times 5)\quad(\times 5)$
$2x = 15$
$(\div 2)\quad(\div 2)$
$x = \dfrac{15}{2}$

4. $\dfrac{9}{x} = 3$
$(\times x)\quad(\times x)$
$9 = 3x$
$(\div 3)\quad(\div 3)$
$3 = x$
$x = 3$

Exercise 2.1A

Solve the following equations:

1. $\dfrac{x}{3} = 5$ 2. $\dfrac{x}{2} = 9$ 3. $\dfrac{x}{7} = 1$ 4. $\dfrac{1}{4}x = 3$

5. $\dfrac{1}{3}x = 11$ 6. $\dfrac{2x}{5} = 4$ 7. $\dfrac{x}{6} = 8$ 8. $\dfrac{1}{4}x = \dfrac{1}{2}$

9. $\dfrac{3}{2}x = 3$ 10. $\dfrac{4}{5}x = 20$ 11. $\dfrac{5}{6}x = 25$ 12. $\dfrac{2}{3}x = 1$

13. $\dfrac{2}{x} = 1$ 14. $\dfrac{4}{7}x = 5$ 15. $\dfrac{2}{5}x = 3$ 16. $\dfrac{6}{x} = 2$

17. $\dfrac{8}{x} = 16$ 18. $\dfrac{9}{2x} = 3$ 19. $\dfrac{5}{3x} = 15$ 20. $\dfrac{10}{3x} = 8$

Worked Examples:

1. $\dfrac{1}{3}x + 4 = 5$
$\dfrac{1}{3}x = 1$
$x = 3$

2. $\dfrac{1}{4}(x - 3) = 5$
$x - 3 = 20$
$x = 23$

3. $5 - \dfrac{3x}{4} = 3$
$5 = 3 + \dfrac{3x}{4}$
$2 = \dfrac{3x}{4}$
$8 = 3x$
$x = \dfrac{8}{3}$

4. $\dfrac{2}{3}(x + 1) = 3$
$2(x + 1) = 9$
$2x + 2 = 9$
$2x = 7$
$x = \dfrac{7}{2}$

NB: When solving equations with brackets, multiply by the denominator first as in examples 2 and 4.

Exercise 2.1B

Solve the following equations:

1. $\dfrac{x}{3} + 2 = 6$

2. $\dfrac{x}{5} - 7 = 1$

3. $\dfrac{x}{2} + 2 = 2$

4. $\dfrac{1}{6}x - 1 = 0$

5. $\dfrac{1}{3}(x + 5) = 1$

6. $\dfrac{3x}{2} - 1 = 4$

7. $6 + \dfrac{x}{3} = 8$

8. $\dfrac{1}{2}(x - 4) = 8$

9. $6 - \dfrac{3}{4}x = 3$

10. $7 + \dfrac{4}{5}x = 4$

11. $\dfrac{5}{3}(x + 2) = 4$

12. $\dfrac{2}{3}x + 8 = 1$

13. $\dfrac{3}{x} - 2 = 1$

14. $1 - \dfrac{4}{7}x = 2$

15. $1 - \dfrac{2}{3}x = 4$

16. $\dfrac{2}{5}(x + 3) = 2$

17. $\dfrac{4}{x} - 2 = 5$

18. $\dfrac{9}{2}(1 - x) = 3$

19. $3 + \dfrac{5}{x} = 1$

20. $\dfrac{5}{2x} - 1 = 9$

To solve equations involving more than one fraction, multiply everything by the **lowest common denominator** of the fractions.

The **Lowest Common Denominator** of two fractions is the lowest common multiple of the denominators. For example, the lowest common multiple of 2,3 and 4 is 12.

Worked Examples:

1. $\dfrac{x}{4} - \dfrac{2}{3} = 1$

$(\times 12) \qquad (\times 12)$

$\dfrac{12x}{4} - \dfrac{24}{3} = 12$

$3x - 8 = 12$

$3x = 20$

$x = \dfrac{20}{3}$

2. $\dfrac{2}{3}(x + 1) = \dfrac{5}{2}$

$(\times 6) \qquad (\times 6)$

$\dfrac{12}{3}(x + 1) = \dfrac{30}{2}$

$4(x + 1) = 15$

$4x + 4 = 15$

$4x = 11$

$x = \dfrac{11}{4}$

3. $\dfrac{x+1}{3} + \dfrac{x}{2} = \dfrac{3}{4}$

$(\times 12) \qquad (\times 12)$

$\dfrac{12(x+1)}{3} + \dfrac{12x}{2} = \dfrac{36}{4}$

$4(x + 1) + 6x = 9$

$4x + 4 + 6x = 9$

$10x + 4 = 9$

$10x = 5$

$x = \dfrac{1}{2}$

NB: In equations with brackets, only the term outside the bracket needs to be multiplied by the lowest common denominator, as in example 2. In example 3, the numerator of the first fraction may be treated like a bracket.

Exercise 2.1C

Solve the following equations:

1. $\dfrac{x}{3} - \dfrac{1}{2} = 1$

2. $\dfrac{x}{2} = \dfrac{1}{2} - 2$

3. $\dfrac{x}{2} - \dfrac{x}{3} = 1$

4. $\dfrac{x}{2} - 3 = \dfrac{x}{5} - 1$

5. $\dfrac{2}{3}x = \dfrac{1}{2}x + 1$

6. $\dfrac{x}{3} = \dfrac{x}{5} - 2$

7. $\frac{2}{3}(x + 1) = \frac{1}{2}(x + 1)$

8. $\frac{1}{2}(x - 2) = \frac{1}{3}(x + 1)$

9. $\frac{1}{3}(x - 4) = \frac{1}{6}(x - 1)$

10. $\frac{3}{4}(x + 2) = \frac{1}{6}(x + 5)$

11. $\frac{3}{5}(x - 7) = \frac{2}{3}(x + 2)$

12. $\frac{5}{6}(x - 3) = \frac{1}{2}(x + 1)$

13. $\frac{1}{4}(x - 8) = \frac{1}{7}(x + 1)$

14. $\frac{x+1}{2} + \frac{x}{3} = 3$

15. $\frac{x-2}{2} + \frac{x}{4} = 4$

16. $\frac{x+5}{3} = \frac{x}{4}$

17. $\frac{x+3}{4} = \frac{2x}{5}$

18. $5 + \frac{x+2}{2} = \frac{1}{3}$

19. $\frac{x}{6} - \frac{x-3}{3} = \frac{1}{4}$

20. $\frac{3(x-5)}{5} = \frac{3}{2}$

21. $\frac{3(x+2)}{5} = \frac{5}{7}$

22. $\frac{4(x+2)}{5} = \frac{5x}{4}$

23. $\frac{2}{7}(x - 1) = \frac{1}{2}(x + 3)$

24. $\frac{x-5}{4} - 1 = \frac{x}{6}$

25. $\frac{2}{3}(x + 1) = \frac{1}{2}(x + 1)$

26. $\frac{4(x+2)}{5} = \frac{5x}{4} - 3$

27. $\frac{4}{5}x - 2 = \frac{2}{9}x + 1$

28. $1 = \frac{2}{3}x - \frac{1}{2}x$

29. $3 - \frac{2}{3}(x - 1) = \frac{1}{4}(x + 6)$

30. $5 - \frac{x-1}{3} = \frac{x}{3}$

2.2 Solving Harder Inequations

Exercise 2.2
Solve the following inequations:

1. $\frac{2}{3}(a + 3) < \frac{1}{2}(a - 2)$

2. $5(b - 2) \leq 3(b + 5)$

3. $8(c - 4) - 3(c + 8) > 2$

4. $d - 4 \leq 6d + 20$

5. $8(e - 3) - 2(e + 5) < 3$

6. $9f - 3 > 12f + 11$

7. $\frac{2(g+1)}{3} + \frac{g}{3} \geq 2$

8. $\frac{3}{5}(h + 5) > \frac{2}{3}(h + 1)$

9. $\frac{2}{3}i + 5 \leq \frac{1}{4}i + 1$

10. $7j - 2 < 9j + 8$

11. $1 - 7k \leq 11 - k$

12. $5 - 3l \geq 2l - 5$

13. $8 > 2 - 7m$

14. $\frac{1}{4}n \geq \frac{2}{3}n + 1$

15. $11 < 4 - 12p$

16. $\frac{2(q-2)}{3} \leq \frac{q}{5}$

17. $6 - 3r \geq 5r - 10$

18. $\frac{2}{3}(1 - s) > \frac{1}{4}(s + 1)$

19. $\frac{2}{3}(3 + t) < \frac{5}{6}(t + 1)$

20. $\frac{1}{3}u \geq \frac{2}{7}u + 5$

21. $2v \leq \frac{3}{5}(2 - v)$

Chapter 5
Substitution and Functions

1.1 Simple Substitution

Substitution is the process of replacing algebraic terms with numerical or equivalent algebraic terms.

Worked Examples:

If $a = 4$, $b = 5$, $c = -3$ and $d = -8$, find:

1. $2a$
   $= 2(4)$
   $= 8$

2. $ab + c$
   $= (4)(5) + (-3)$
   $= 20 - 3$
   $= 17$

3. $3ab + 2cd$
   $= 3(4)(5) + 2(-3)(-8)$
   $= 3(20) + 2(24)$
   $= 60 + 48$
   $= 108$

NB: When substituting negative values into an expression, it is good practice to use brackets, as in examples 2 and 3.

Exercise 1.1A

If $a = 3$, $b = 4$, $c = -2$, $d = -5$ and $e = -3$ find:

1. $3a$
2. $2b$
3. $5c$
4. $3d$

5. $6e$
6. $a + b$
7. $b + c$
8. $d + e$

9. $2b + d$
10. $3d - c$
11. $4a - e$
12. $5b + d$

13. $b - e$
14. $e - c$
15. $3d - 2c$
16. $5a - 3d$

17. $de + a$
18. $bc - d$
19. $3cd - 2ae$
20. $5bc - 2de$

Worked Examples:

If $a = 4$, $b = 5$, $c = -3$ and $d = -8$, find:

1. $\dfrac{4b-d}{a}$
   $= \dfrac{4(5)-(-8)}{(4)}$
   $= \dfrac{28}{4}$
   $= 7$

2. $bd \div 2a$
   $= (5)(-8) \div 2(4)$
   $= -40 \div 8$
   $= -5$

3. $b(a - d)$
   $= 5(4 - (-8))$
   $= 5(12)$
   $= 60$

Exercise 1.1B

If $a = 5$, $b = 3$, $c = -4$, $d = 6$, $e = -1$ and $f = 2$ find:

1. $\dfrac{a+e}{f}$
2. $\dfrac{d-c}{f}$
3. $\dfrac{d-e+f}{b}$
4. $\dfrac{d+ce}{a}$

5. $8a \div c$

6. $12a \div d$

7. $f - ed$

8. $bc \times a$

9. $d + ce$

10. $5f \div a$

11. $\dfrac{abf}{d}$

12. $5(b + d)$

13. $b(f - e)$

14. $f(d - c) \div a$

15. $5(bc + d) - 4e$

16. $5(f - c) + 4e$

17. $d(a - b) - f(d + c)$

18. $\dfrac{a(f+b)}{d+e}$

19. $\dfrac{3(f-e)}{d-b}$

20. $\dfrac{4(d-c)-5e}{ab}$

Worked Examples:

If $a = 2, b = 4, c = -3$ and $d = -4$, find:

1. $ba^2 \div 2$
$= (4)(2)^2 \div 2$
$= 16 \div 2$
$= 8$

2. $(ab)^2$
$= (2 \times 4)^2$
$= (8)^2$
$= 64$

3. $(a - d)(b + c)$
$= (2 - (-4))(4 + (-3))$
$= (6)(1)$
$= 6$

Exercise 1.1C

If $a = 2, b = 3, c = 4, d = 5, e = -1, f = -2, g = -5$ find:

1. $3a^2 \div b$

2. $2b^2 \div a$

3. $ac^2 \div f$

4. $ag^2 \div d$

5. $(ab)^2$

6. $(af)^2$

7. $(de)^2$

8. $(fg)^2$

9. a^2b

10. c^2e

11. $a(2e)^2$

12. c^2e^2

13. a^3b^2

14. $(d - c)^2$

15. $(g - f)^2$

16. $(c - a)^3$

17. $(b + c)(d - f)$

18. $(c - g)(c - a)^2$

19. $(2g)^2 - 2g^2$

20. $cb^2 - e(g)^2$

21. $\sqrt{ad + ab}$

22. $\sqrt{deg}$

23. $\sqrt{aef}$

24. $\sqrt{cdeg}$

2.1 Substitution into Formulae

Some common formulae are given below:

Volume of a Cylinder: $V = \pi r^2 h$

Volume of a Cone: $V = \frac{1}{3}\pi r^2 h$

Volume of a Sphere: $V = \frac{4}{3}\pi r^3$

Surface area of a Sphere: $A = 4\pi r^2$

In the formulae:
$'r'$ is the radius
$'h'$ is the height
$'\pi'$ is 'Pi' which is 3.14159 ...

> **Worked Example:**
>
> Use the formula to find the volume of a cylinder with a radius of 3 units, and a height of 5 units.
>
> $V = \pi r^2 h$
> $V = \pi \times (3)^2 \times (5)$
> $V = 141.4\ units^3\ (to\ 1\ d.p.)$
>
> NB: When using a calculator, three lines of working are sufficient.

Exercise 2.1A – Use a Calculator

Substitute the following values into the formula: $V = \pi r^2 h$

1. $r = 2, h = 4$
2. $r = 3, h = 5$
3. $r = 3, h = 7$
4. $r = 10, h = 6$

5. $r = 6, h = 3$
6. $r = 5, h = 11$
7. $r = 12, h = 22$
8. $r = 5, h = 10$

Substitute the following values into the formula: $V = \frac{1}{3}\pi r^2 h$

9. $r = 6, h = 3$
10. $r = 2, h = 4$
11. $r = 5, h = 1$
12. $r = 11, h = 15$

13. $r = 10, h = 8$
14. $r = 7, h = 0.5$
15. $r = 5, h = 9$
16. $r = 2, h = 13$

Substitute the following values into the formula: $V = \frac{4}{3}\pi r^3$

17. $r = 2$
18. $r = 3$
19. $r = 8$
20. $r = 10$

21. $r = 6$
22. $r = 5$
23. $r = 12$
24. $r = 9$

Substitute the following values into the formula: $A = 4\pi r^2$

25. $r = 7$
26. $r = 11$
27. $r = 2$
28. $r = 1$

29. $r = 15$
30. $r = 9$
31. $r = 10$
32. $r = 12$

Substitute the following values into the formula: $h = \frac{3V}{\pi r^2}$

33. $V = 180, r = 3$
34. $V = 400, r = 12$
35. $V = 550, r = 10$
36. $V = 40, r = 6$

37. $V = 60, r = 2$
38. $V = 1000, r = 9$
39. $V = 70, r = 6$
40. $V = 4000, r = 15$

Substitute the following values into the formula: $r = \sqrt{\dfrac{V}{\pi h}}$

41. $V = 200, h = 3$
42. $V = 500, h = 6$
43. $V = 110, h = 4$
44. $V = 760, h = 5$

45. $V = 60, h = 2$
46. $V = 1000, h = 9$
47. $V = 70, h = 6$
48. $V = 4000, h = 15$

The formula $x = \frac{-b \pm \sqrt{b^2 - 4ac}}{2a}$ is known as the **Quadratic Formula** and is used to find roots of

quadratic functions when factorising is difficult

(see **chapter 10, section 2.4, page 89**).

> **NB:** The mathematical symbol $\pm$ means that both operations $+$ and $-$ need to be carried out.

Worked Example:

Use the quadratic formula to find x to 1 decimal place, when $a = 4$, $b = -5$ and $c = -3$.

$$x = \frac{-b \pm \sqrt{b^2 - 4ac}}{2a}$$

$$x = \frac{-(-5) \pm \sqrt{(-5)^2 - 4(4)(-3)}}{2(4)}$$

$$x = \frac{5 + \sqrt{73}}{4} \qquad x = \frac{5 - \sqrt{73}}{4}$$

$$x = 3.4 \qquad\qquad x = -0.9$$

Exercise 2.1B – Use a Calculator

Substitute the following values into the formula: $x = \frac{-b \pm \sqrt{b^2 - 4ac}}{2a}$

1. $a = 4, b = 4, c = -1$

2. $a = 2, b = 4, c = -1$

3. $a = 3, b = 2, c = -1$

4. $a = 1, b = 3, c = -2$

5. $a = 2, b = -3, c = 1$

6. $a = 3, b = 8, c = 1$

7. $a = -3, b = 4, c = 1$

8. $a = 1, b = -7, c = 3$

9. $a = -4, b = 3, c = 2$

10. $a = 2, b = 9, c = -3$

11. $a = -2, b = -8, c = 1$

12. $a = -1, b = -6, c = 5$

13. $a = 3, b = 5, c = 1$

14. $a = -4, b = 10, c = 3$

15. $a = 10, b = 11, c = -1$

2.2 Function Notation

Function notation is usually written in the form $f(x)$ or $g(x)$ meaning a function 'f' or 'g' of x. In such

notation, an x value is input into the function and the result is $f(x)$.

Worked Examples: If $f(x) = 2x + 1$ and $g(x) = 3x^2 - 2x$

1. Find $f(x)$ when $x = 2$

$f(x) = 2x + 1$
$f(2) = 2(2) + 1$
$f(2) = 4 + 1$
$f(2) = 5$

2. Find $g(x)$ when $x = -3$

$g(x) = 3x^2 - 2x$
$g(-3) = 3(-3)^2 - 2(-3)$
$g(-3) = 3(9)^2 + 6$
$g(-3) = 33$

3. Find $f(-5)$

$f(x) = 2x + 1$
$f(-5) = 2(-5) + 1$
$f(-5) = -10 + 1$
$f(-5) = -9$

4. Find $g\left(\frac{1}{2}\right)$

$g(x) = 3x^2 - 2x$
$g\left(\frac{1}{2}\right) = 3\left(\frac{1}{2}\right)^2 - 2\left(\frac{1}{2}\right)$
$g\left(\frac{1}{2}\right) = \frac{3}{4} - 1$
$g\left(\frac{1}{2}\right) = -\frac{1}{4}$

Exercise 2.2

For the following functions:

$$f(x) = 3x - 1 \qquad g(x) = 2x + 2 \qquad h(x) = 5 - 8x \qquad k(x) = 3x - 5$$

Find:

1. $f(x)$ when $x = 3$
2. $g(x)$ when $x = 3$
3. $f(x)$ when $x = 2$
4. $h(x)$ when $x = 5$

5. $g(x)$ when $x = 4$
6. $k(x)$ when $x = 2$
7. $h(x)$ when $x = 7$
8. $f(x)$ when $x = 4$

9. $h(x)$ when $x = 4$
10. $f(x)$ when $x = -1$
11. $k(x)$ when $x = -6$
12. $g(x)$ when $x = -3$

13. $k(x)$ when $x = -5$
14. $h(x)$ when $x = -4$
15. $g(x)$ when $x = -2$
16. $k(x)$ when $x = -2$

For the following functions:

$$f(x) = x^2 - 1 \qquad g(x) = x^2 + 4 \qquad h(x) = 3x^2 - 2x + 1 \qquad k(x) = \frac{x^2 - 2}{3x + 5}$$

Find:

17. $g(x)$ when $x = 3$
18. $f(x)$ when $x = 3$
19. $h(x)$ when $x = 2$
20. $k(x)$ when $x = 5$

21. $f(x)$ when $x = 4$
22. $h(x)$ when $x = 3$
23. $g(x)$ when $x = 7$
24. $f(x)$ when $x = 6$

25. $k(x)$ when $x = 4$
26. $g(x)$ when $x = -1$
27. $f(x)$ when $x = -6$
28. $h(x)$ when $x = -3$

29. $h(x)$ when $x = -5$
30. $k(x)$ when $x = -3$
31. $g(x)$ when $x = -2$
32. $k(x)$ when $x = -2$

For the following functions:

$$f(x) = 7x^2 - 2x \qquad g(x) = \frac{x^2}{2} + 3 \qquad h(x) = 5x^2 + 2x - 3 \qquad k(x) = \frac{x^2 - 2x + 1}{x - 5}$$

Find:

33. $g(2)$
34. $f(-2)$
35. $h(-2)$
36. $k(8)$

37. $f(4)$
38. $h(4)$
39. $g(6)$
40. $f(-3)$

41. $k(-3)$
42. $g(-2)$
43. $f\left(\frac{1}{2}\right)$
44. $h\left(\frac{1}{3}\right)$

45. $h(-1)$
46. $k\left(\frac{1}{2}\right)$
47. $g\left(-\frac{1}{2}\right)$
48. $k\left(\frac{1}{3}\right)$

3.1 Composite Functions

Composite Functions consist of more than one function. Substitution is used to determine the resulting composite function when two functions are given. Instead of substituting a value in place of the x term, an entire function is substituted.

Worked Examples: If $f(x) = 2x + 1$ and $g(x) = 3x^2 - 2x$

1. Find $f(g(x))$

$$f(g(x)) = 2(3x^2 - 2x) + 1$$
$$f(g(x)) = 6x^2 - 4x + 1$$

2. Find $g(f(x))$

$$g(f(x)) = 3(2x + 1)^2 - 2(2x + 1)$$
$$g(f(x)) = 3(4x^2 + 4x + 1) - 4x - 2$$
$$g(f(x)) = 12x^2 + 12x + 3 - 4x - 2$$
$$g(f(x)) = 12x^2 + 8x + 1$$

Exercise 3.1A

For the following functions:

$$f(x) = 3x - 1 \qquad g(x) = 2x + 2 \qquad h(x) = 5 - 8x \qquad k(x) = 3x - 5$$

Find:

1. $f(g(x))$
2. $g(f(x))$
3. $f(h(x))$
4. $h(f(x))$

5. $g(h(x))$
6. $h(g(x))$
7. $h(k(x))$
8. $k(h(x))$

9. $k(g(x))$
10. $g(k(x))$
11. $k(f(x))$
12. $f(k(x))$

For the following functions:

$$f(x) = 2x - 1 \qquad g(x) = x^2 + 4 \qquad h(x) = 3x^2 - 2 \qquad k(x) = \frac{2}{3x+5}$$

Find:

13. $f(g(x))$
14. $g(f(x))$
15. $f(h(x))$
16. $h(f(x))$

17. $g(h(x))$
18. $h(g(x))$
19. $k(h(x))$
20. $k(g(x))$

21. $k(f(x))$
22. $g(g(x))$
23. $f(f(x))$
24. $h(h(x))$

For the following functions:

$$f(x) = \frac{1}{x-2} \qquad g(x) = \frac{2}{3-x} \qquad h(x) = \frac{4}{x-5} \qquad k(x) = \frac{3}{x+2}$$

Find:

25. $k(f(x))$
26. $k(g(x))$
27. $k(h(x))$
28. $k(k(x))$

29. $g(f(x))$
30. $g(h(x))$
31. $g(k(x))$
32. $g(g(x))$

33. $f(g(x))$
34. $f(h(x))$
35. $f(f(x))$
36. $h(f(x))$

Worked Examples: If $f(x) = 2x + 1$ and $g(x) = 3x^2 - 2x$

1. Find $f(g(3))$
$$g(3) = 3(3)^2 - 2(3) = 21$$
$$f(g(3)) = 2(21) + 1$$
$$f(g(x)) = 43$$

2. Find $g(f(-2))$
$$f(-2) = 2(-2) + 1 = -3$$
$$g(f(-2)) = 3(-3)^2 - 2(-3)$$
$$g(f(x)) = 27 + 6$$
$$g(f(x)) = 33$$

Exercise 3.1B

For the following functions:

$$f(x) = 2x - 3 \qquad g(x) = x^2 - 1 \qquad h(x) = \frac{1}{x+1} \qquad k(x) = 2x + 5$$

Find:

1. $f(g(-2))$

2. $g(f(3))$

3. $f(h(-4))$

4. $h(f(5))$

5. $g(h(-2))$

6. $h(g(5))$

7. $h(k(2))$

8. $k(h(2))$

9. $k(g(3))$

10. $g(k(2))$

11. $k(f(-5))$

12. $f(k(-4))$

For the following functions:

$$f(x) = 5x - 1 \qquad g(x) = x^2 + 2 \qquad h(x) = 3x^2 - x \qquad k(x) = \frac{2}{x+4}$$

Find:

13. $f(g(1))$

14. $g(f(-1))$

15. $f(h(2))$

16. $h(f(2))$

17. $g(h(-2))$

18. $h(g(3))$

19. $k(h(-3))$

20. $k(g(3))$

21. $k(f(-5))$

22. $g(g(-3))$

23. $k(f(-4))$

24. $k(h(-5))$

Chapter 6
Solving Equations 2 – Simultaneous Linear Equations

2.1 Simultaneous Equations by Substitution

Chapter 4 involved solving equations with one unknown, but often it is necessary to solve more than one equation with more than one unknown simultaneously. This process involves finding values for all the unknowns, for which all the equations are true.

For simultaneous equations involving two unknowns, there are two methods: solving by **substitution** or by **elimination**.

Simultaneous equations can be solved by **substitution** if one of the equations has an unknown with a coefficient equal to one, or if the unknown is of equal value in both equations.

NB: The coefficient of a term is the numerical part of the term. For an algebraic term with no explicit numerical part, the coefficient is 1.

Worked Examples:

1. Solve the equations $y = 5x + 3$ and $y = 2x + 6$ simultaneously.

$\quad$ *Substitute* $y = 5x + 3$ into $y = 2x + 5$
$$5x + 3 = 2x + 6 \quad \text{(as equations are equal to 'y', they can be set equal to one another)}$$
$$3x + 3 = 6$$
$$3x = 3$$
$$x = 1$$
$\quad$ *Substitute* $x = 1$ into $y = 5x + 3$
$$y = 5(1) + 3$$
$$y = 8$$
$\quad$ Solution: $x = 1$ and $y = 8$.

2. Solve the equations $3y + 2x = 4$ and $y = 5x + 7$ simultaneously.

$\quad$ *Substitute* $y = 5x + 7$ into $3y + 2x = 4$
$$3(5x + 7) + 2x = 4$$
$$15x + 21 + 2x = 4$$
$$17x = -17$$
$$x = -1$$
$\quad$ *Substitute* $x = -1$ into $y = 5x + 7$ (this is the easier equation to solve)
$$y = 5(-1) + 7$$
$$y = 2$$
$\quad$ Solution: $x = -1$ and $y = 2$.

Exercise 2.1A

Solve the following systems of equations by substitution:

1. $x + 2y = 4$
   $y = 2x - 3$

2. $5x + y = 3$
   $y = x - 3$

3. $2x + 2y = 2$
   $y = x - 7$

4. $6x + 5y = 22$
   $y = 3x - 4$

5. $2x + 2y = 8$
   $y = 2x - 14$

6. $5x - 3y = 7$
   $y = x + 1$

7. $7x - 2y = 9$
   $y = 5x - 6$

8. $3x + 3y = 21$
   $y = 16 - 2x$

9. $y = x - 2$
   $y = 2x - 9$

10. $y = 3x + 24$
    $y = x - 4$

11. $y = 5x + 11$
    $y = x + 3$

12. $y = 25 + x$
    $y = 2x + 43$

13. $x + 2y = -6$
    $y = 3x + 11$

14. $x - 3y = -5$
    $y = x + 11$

15. $7x + 8y = 3$
    $y = 5x + 18$

16. $7x + 18y = 4$
    $y = x + 3$

17. $y = 2x + 37$
    $y = -3x - 38$

18. $y = 5x + 19$
    $y = 2x + 7$

19. $y = -x - 1$
    $y = 5x + 23$

20. $y = 4 - 2x$
    $y = 3x + 19$

21. $3x + y = 5$
    $y = 10 - 2x$

22. $4x + 2y = 2$
    $y = 6x + 5$

23. $7x + 2y = 9$
    $y = 12 - x$

24. $2x - 2y = -30$
    $y = 6 - 2x$

25. $y = 2x - 3$
    $y = -4x$

26. $y = x + 5$
    $y = -2x + 14$

27. $y = -x + 3$
    $y = 4x + 23$

28. $y = 12 - 2x$
    $y = 6x + 16$

29. $5x + y = 19$
    $y = 16 - 2x$

30. $4x + 6y = 10$
    $y = 8x + 6$

31. $6x + 2y = 4$
    $y = 1 - x$

32. $8x - 2y = -6$
    $y = 5 - 4x$

When solving simultaneous equations, sometimes it is preferable to rearrange the equations to solve by substitution, rather than by elimination.

Worked Example:

Solve the equations $3x + y = 9$ and $y - x = 1$ simultaneously.

Rearrange equations:

$3x + y = 9$ $y - x = 1$
    $y = 9 - 3x$ $y = x + 1$

Substitute $y = 9 - 3x$ into $y = x + 1$

$9 - 3x = x + 1$ (as equations are equal to 'y', they can be set equal to one another)
    $9 = 4x + 1$
    $8 = 4x$
    $x = 2$

Substitute $x = 2$ into $y = x + 1$
    $y = 2 + 1$
    $y = 3$

Solution: $x = 2$ and $y = 3$.

Exercise 2.1B

Solve the following systems of equations by substitution, by first rearranging:

1. $x + 3y = 4$
   $y - 2x = -1$

2. $4x + y = 3$
   $5x - y = 6$

3. $x + y = 5$
   $2y = x + 1$

4. $7x + y = 9$
   $2x - y = 0$

5. $3x + 2y = 9$
   $y + x = 4$

6. $4x - 5y = 11$
   $2x - y = 7$

7. $x - 2y = 4$
   $3y + 5x = 7$

8. $4x + 3y = 14$
   $2y - x + 9 = 0$

9. $y + x - 8 = 0$
   $y = 4x - 22$

10. $y - 3x = -3$
    $4x + 2y = -16$

11. $5x - 2y = -11$
    $2x + 2y = -10$

12. $4y + 3x = 1$
    $2x - y - 8 = 0$

13. $2y = x + 3$
    $3x + y = -16$

14. $x - 3y = 4$
    $5x + 3y = -16$

15. $2x + 8y = 14$
    $5x - y + 28 = 0$

16. $6x + y = -11$
    $x - 2y = -4$

17. $2x - 5y = 1$
    $x - 3y = 0$

18. $5x + 6y = 22$
    $10 - 2x = 3y$

19. $2y - x = -8$
    $4y + x - 5 = 0$

20. $12x - y = 4$
    $8x + 5y = 14$

2.2 Simultaneous Equations by Elimination

Simultaneous equations can always be solved by **elimination**. This process requires manipulation of equations in order to ensure coefficients of a chosen variable have the same magnitude, then addition or subtraction of equations to eliminate the chosen variable.

NB: This book will concentrate on always adding the equations, as this avoids most mistakes with negatives numbers. The coefficients of the middle terms in each equation should have *the same number with a different sign*, then the system of equations may be added to eliminate the term.

Worked Examples:

1. Solve the system of equations by elimination
$$3x + y = 11$$
$$2x - y = 9.$$
Solution:

$$
\begin{array}{ll}
3x + y = 11 & \text{(A)} \\
2x - y = 9 & \text{(B)} \\
\hline
\text{(A)+(B)} \quad 5x \quad\ = 20 & \\
x = 4 &
\end{array}
$$

Substitute $x = 4$ into **(A)**.
$$3(4) + y = 11$$
$$12 + y = 11$$
$$y = -1$$

Solution: $x = 4$ and $y = -1$.

2. Solve the system of equations by elimination
$$5x + y = 17$$
$$3x + y = 11.$$
Solution:

$$
\begin{array}{ll}
5x + y = 17 & \text{(A)} \\
3x + y = 11 & \text{(B)} \\
\text{(B)} \times -1 \quad -3x - y = -11 & \text{(C)} \\
\hline
\text{(A)+(C)} \quad 2x \quad\ = 6 & \\
x = 3 &
\end{array}
$$

Substitute $x = 3$ into **(A)**.
$$5(3) + y = 17$$
$$15 + y = 17$$
$$y = 2$$

Solution: $x = 3$ and $y = 2$.

Exercise 2.2A

Solve the following systems of equations by elimination:

1. $x + y = 3$
    $x - y = 1$

2. $3x + y = 8$
    $2x - y = 2$

3. $5x + y = 7$
    $3x - y = 1$

4. $4x + y = 14$
    $x - y = 1$

5. $3x + y = 3$
    $x - y = 5$

6. $4x + y = 10$
    $x - y = 5$

7. $5x + y = -9$
    $x - y = -3$

8. $3x + y = 7$
    $x - y = 5$

9. $2x + y = 10$
    $3x - y = 10$

10. $5x + y = -8$
    $2x - y = 1$

11. $2x + y = -6$
    $5x - y = -8$

12. $6x + y = 23$
    $5x - y = 21$

13. $3x + 2y = -3$
    $2x - 2y = -22$

14. $2x + 3y = -2$
    $x - 3y = 8$

15. $4x + 2y = 2$
    $x - 2y = 8$

16. $7x + 5y = 19$
    $2x - 5y = -1$

17. $4x + 2y = -12$
    $3x - 2y = 26$

18. $5x + 2y = 48$
    $3x - 2y = 16$

19. $4x + 2y = 32$
    $2x - 2y = -2$

20. $4x + 4y = 8$
    $x - 4y = 7$

21. $3x + y = -11$
    $3x - y = -1$

22. $3x + 5y = 4$
    $2x - 5y = 36$

23. $5x + 9y = -3$
    $x - 9y = 21$

24. $2x - 4y = 6$
    $x - 4y = 4$

Exercise 2.2B

Solve the following systems of equations by elimination:

1. $x + y = 2$
    $2x + y = 3$

2. $4x + y = 10$
    $2x + y = 6$

3. $3x + y = 5$
    $5x + y = 7$

4. $3x + y = 11$
    $7x + y = 23$

5. $x + y = -1$
    $6x + y = 9$

6. $3x + y = 7$
    $x + y = 1$

7. $4x + y = -7$
    $x + y = -1$

8. $3x + y = 7$
    $x + y = 1$

9. $2x + y = 10$
    $x + y = 6$

10. $5x + y = -8$
    $x + y = -4$

11. $2x + y = -6$
    $x + y = -4$

12. $6x + y = 23$
    $3x + y = 11$

13. $3x + 2y = -3$
    $x + 2y = 7$

14. $x + 3y = -4$
    $3x + 3y = 0$

15. $5x + 2y = 4$
    $x + 2y = -4$

16. $7x + 5y = 19$
    $3x + 5y = 11$

17. $4x + 2y = -12$
    $3x + 2y = -14$

18. $4x + 2y = 28$
    $x + 2y = 13$

19. $3x + 2y = 27$
    $x + 2y = 17$

20. $2x + 4y = 2$
    $5x - 4y = 19$

Worked Example:

3. Solve, by elimination, the system of equations

$$3x + 3y = 15$$
$$3x - y = 11.$$

Solution:

$$
\begin{array}{ll}
3x + 3y = 15 & \textbf{(A)} \\
3x - y = 11 & \textbf{(B)}
\end{array}
$$

$$
\begin{array}{ll}
\textbf{(B)} \times 3 & \underline{9x - 3y = 33} \quad \textbf{(C)} \\
\textbf{(A)+(C)} & 12x \quad\quad = 48 \\
& x = 4
\end{array}
$$

Substitute $x = 4$ into **(A)**.

$$3(4) + 3y = 15$$
$$12 + 3y = 15$$
$$3y = 3$$
$$y = 1$$

Solution: $x = 4$ and $y = 1$.

4. Solve, by elimination, the system of equations

$$6x + 2y = 16$$
$$4x + y = 11.$$

Solution:

$$
\begin{array}{ll}
6x + 2y = 16 & \textbf{(A)} \\
4x + y = 11 & \textbf{(B)}
\end{array}
$$

$$
\begin{array}{ll}
\textbf{(B)} \times -2 & \underline{-8x - 2y = -22} \quad \textbf{(C)} \\
\textbf{(A)+(C)} & -2x \quad\quad = -6 \\
& x = 3
\end{array}
$$

Substitute $x = 3$ into **(A)**.

$$6(3) + 2y = 16$$
$$18 + 2y = 16$$
$$2y = -2$$
$$y = -1$$

Solution: $x = 3$ and $y = -1$.

NB: In all the worked examples the middle terms in each equation are scaled to have *the same number with a different sign*. Sometimes it can be easier to scale the first terms.

Exercise 2.2C

Solve the following systems of equations by elimination:

1. $x + 3y = 11$
   $x - y = -1$

2. $x + 2y = 7$
   $2x - y = -1$

3. $5x + 4y = 28$
   $3x - y = 10$

4. $4x + 3y = 6$
   $3x - y = 11$

5. $4x + 2y = -6$
   $x - y = -3$

6. $3x + 3y = 21$
   $2x - y = 8$

7. $4x + 3y = -6$
   $x - y = -5$

8. $4x + 5y = 15$
   $x - y = 6$

9. $2x + 5y = 17$
   $5x + y = 31$

10. $2x + 3y = -14$
    $3x + y = -14$

11. $2x + 2y = 2$
    $3x + y = -5$

12. $4x + 4y = -12$
    $3x + y = 1$

13. $2x + 2y = 0$
    $3x + y = -12$

14. $2x + 3y = 3$
    $4x - y = 13$

15. $4x + 6y = 17$
    $x - 2y = 6$

16. $2x + 2y = 10$
    $3x + y = 11$

17. $4x + 4y = -2$
    $3x + 2y = 1$

18. $3x + 2y = 21$
    $5x - 4y = 24$

19. $4x + 3y = 19$
    $2x - y = 2$

20. $2x + 3y = 1$
    $4x - y = 16$

21. $2x + 2y = -6$
    $6x - 4y = 7$

22. $3x + 2y = 8$
    $x - 6y = 16$

23. $3x + 2y = 11$
    $x - 4y = 20$

24. $4x - 4y = 11$
    $8x + 2y = 17$

Worked Example:

5. Solve, by elimination, the system of equations
$$3x + 3y = 9$$
$$5x - 2y = 1.$$

Solution:

	$3x + 3y = 9$	**(A)**
	$5x - 2y = 1$	**(B)**
	$6x + 6y = 18$	**(C)**
(B) × 3	$15x - 6y = 3$	**(D)**
(C)+(D)	$21x \quad\quad = 21$	
	$x = 1$	

Substitute $x = 1$ *into* **(A)**.
$$3(1) + 3y = 9$$
$$3 + 3y = 9$$
$$3y = 6$$
$$y = 2$$
Solution: $x = 1$ and $y = 2$.

6. Solve, by elimination, the system of equations
$$4x + 3y = 9$$
$$2x + 5y = 1.$$

Solution:

	$4x + 3y = 9$	**(A)**
	$2x + 5y = 1$	**(B)**
(A) × 5	$20x + 15y = 45$	**(C)**
(B) × −3	$-6x - 15y = -3$	**(D)**
(C)+(D)	$14x \quad\quad = 42$	
	$x = 3$	

Substitute $x = 3$ *into* **(A)**.
$$4(3) + 3y = 9$$
$$12 + 3y = 9$$
$$3y = -3$$
$$y = -1$$
Solution: $x = 3$ and $y = -1$.

Exercise 2.2D

Solve the following systems of equations by elimination:

1. $x + 3y = 10$
$2x - 2y = -4$

2. $x + 2y = 8$
$4x - y = 5$

3. $5x + 3y = 27$
$2x - 2y = -2$

4. $3x - 2y = 14$
$x - 5y = 9$

5. $3x - 2y = -4$
$x - 3y = 1$

6. $4x + 4y = 20$
$2x - 3y = 0$

7. $5x - 5y = -20$
$3x + 3y = -6$

8. $4x + 2y = 16$
$3x - 3y = 21$

9. $2x + 5y = -1$
$5x + 2y = 8$

10. $6x - 2y = 40$
$x - 3y = 12$

11. $4x + 2y = 20$
$x + 5y = 23$

12. $5x - 4y = -2$
$2x + 3y = 13$

13. $6x + 7y = 45$
$x + 2y = 10$

14. $5x - 2y = 13$
$3x - 5y = -15$

15. $5x + 7y = 69$
$2x + 9y = 71$

16. $2x - 6y = 18$
$3x - 7y = 23$

17. $4x - 4y = 16$
$2x + 9y = -14$

18. $3x + 2y = 24$
$5x - 3y = 21$

19. $6x + 3y = 39$
$2x - 2y = 4$

20. $4x + 3y = -4$
$8x - y = 6$

21. $2x + 2y = 2$
$6x - 4y = 21$

22. $3x + 2y = 13$
$x - 6y = 1$

23. $3x + 2y = 10$
$x - 4y = 15$

24. $4x - 4y = 16$
$6x + 2y = 20$

25. $4x + 4y = -2$
$3x + 2y = 0$

26. $3x - 2y = 5$
$5x - 3y = 8.5$

27. $3x - 3y = 6$
$2x - 5y = -2$

28. $2x + 3y = 12$
$5x + 2y = 19$

29. $7x + 2y = 20$
    $2x - 7y = 9.5$

30. $5x - 3y = 22$
    $3x + 5y = 20$

31. $6x - 5y = -4$
    $5x - 7y = -9$

32. $11x - 7y = 73$
    $13x + 9y = 69$

2.3 Forming Equations to Solve Simultaneously

Exercise 2.3A

<u>By forming two equations</u>, solve the following problems:

1. Three pencils and two rubbers cost £0.76, four pencils and five rubbers cost £1.48. Calculate how much one pencil costs and one rubber costs.

2. The local cinema has standard and superior seats. On Thursday they sell 50 standard and 5 superior seats and sales amount to £317.50. On Friday they sell 100 standard and 20 superior seats and ticket sales amount to £720.

   By forming two equations, calculate how much 1 standard seat costs and how much 1 superior seat costs.

3. A plane seats 200 passengers. A standard class ticket costs £120 and a business class ticket costs £250. If the plane is full, the ticket sales are £30,500.

   By forming two equations, calculate how many standard and how many business class tickets there are.

4. James has a pay-as-you-go phone. One day he sends 30 text messages and uses 45 minutes and it costs him £6.90. Another day he sends 25 text messages and uses 9 minutes and it costs him £2.33.

   By forming two equations, calculate how much 1 text message costs and 1 minute costs.

5. Three apples and two oranges cost £1.35, five apples and six oranges cost £3.05. Calculate how much one apple and one orange costs.

6. John sells raffle tickets. The first day he sells seven strips and twelve individual tickets for £11.20. The next day he sells sixteen strips and thirty six individual tickets for £28.60.

   By forming two equations, calculate how much 1 strip and 1 individual ticket cost.

7. A bus seats 57 passengers. A standard ticket costs £15 and an extra legroom ticket costs £25. If the bus is full, the ticket sales are £975.

   By forming two equations, calculate how many standard and extra legroom tickets there are.

8. Shazia saves £1 and £2 coins in a jar. There are 50 coins in the jar. Altogether there is £80 in the jar. How many £1 coins and how many £2 coins are there?

9. Jacus takes part in a Maths competition. He gains 5 points for every correct answer and loses 2 points for every incorrect answer. He answers 15 questions and scores 19 points. How many questions does he answer correctly and how many incorrectly?

10. Jeremiah stays in a Bed & Breakfast, he stays for three nights and has breakfast on two mornings. His bill is £136. Jamila stays in the same Bed & Breakfast for five nights and has breakfast on three mornings. Her bill is £224. How much does it cost for one night and how much for one breakfast?

11. A group of friends go out for dessert. Between them they buy 4 ice creams and 5 waffles, and they pay £36.50. Another group buy 3 ice creams and 7 waffles, and they pay £42. Calculate the price of 1 ice cream and of 1 waffle.

12. Kieran has a pay-as-you-go phone. One day he sends 150 text messages and uses 5 minutes and it costs him £5.50. Another day he sends 200 text messages and uses 2 minutes and it costs him £6.40.

    By forming two equations, calculate how much 1 text message costs and 1 minute costs.

13. Three chocolate bars and two bags of crisps cost £2.85, four chocolate bars and one bag of crisps cost £2.80. Calculate how much one chocolate bar costs and one bag of crisps costs.

14. Javid saves 20p and 50p coins in a piggy bank. In the piggy bank, he has 220 coins altogether and their value is £80. Calculate how many 50p and how many 20p coins he has in the piggy bank.

15. Some friends go to a cafe and buy three coffees and two cakes for £9.90. Another group of friends buy five coffees and six cakes for £19.70.

    By forming two equations, calculate how much 1 coffee and 1 cake cost.

16. A plane seats 320 passengers and is made up of first class and standard class seats. A first class ticket costs £1200 and a standard class ticket costs £640. If the plane is full, the ticket sales are £227,200.

    By forming two equations, calculate how many first class and standard class tickets there are.

17. A concert hall seats 520 people. The hall is made up of 220 superior seats and 300 standard seats. One evening the hall is full and the ticket sales amount to £31,900. Find how much 1 text superior seat costs and 1 standard seat costs.

18. Six pens and two pencils cost £5.40, four pens and five pencils cost £5.25. Calculate how much one pen costs and one pencil costs.

19. A family go to a burger restaurant and buy four burgers and six fries and their bill costs £29.40. Another family buy three burgers and three fries and their bill costs £19.20. Another family buy five burgers and two fries. How much is their bill?

20. Two teams compete in a Mathletes' event at school. For each correct question points are awarded and for each incorrect question, points are deducted. The first team answers 7 correctly and 4 incorrectly and score 23 points. The second team answer 10 correctly and 1 incorrectly and score 47 points

    By forming two equations, calculate how many points are awarded for a correct answer and how many are deducted for an incorrect answer.

21. Zahid has a pay-as-you-go phone. One day he sends 75 text messages and uses 30 minutes and it costs him £8.25. Another day he sends 28 text messages and uses 5 minutes and it costs him £2.15.

    By forming two equations, calculate how much 1 text message and 1 minute costs.

22. Some friends go to a cafe and buy four coffees and two cakes for £14.90. Another group of friends buy three coffees and four cakes for £16.05. A couple also buy two coffees and two cakes. How much is their bill?

23. The local cinema has standard and superior seats. On Thursday they sell 32 standard and 15 superior seats and tickets sales amount to £428.20. On Friday they sell 112 standard and 45 superior seats and ticket sales amount to £1422.20.

    By forming two equations, calculate how much 1 standard seat costs and 1 superior seat costs.

24. Some friends go for pizza and buy two pizzas and four drinks for £26.60. Another group of friends buy three pizzas and five drinks for £38. A couple buy one pizza and two drinks. How much is their bill?

Exercise 2.3B

<u>By forming two equations</u>, solve the following problems:

1.

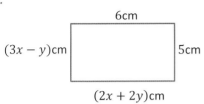

6cm

$(3x − y)$cm

5cm

$(2x + 2y)$cm

2.

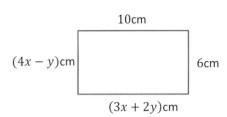

10cm

$(4x − y)$cm

6cm

$(3x + 2y)$cm

3.

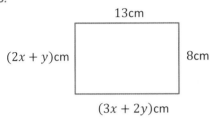

13cm

$(2x + y)$cm

8cm

$(3x + 2y)$cm

4.

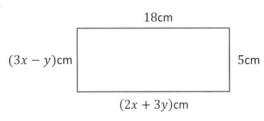

18cm

$(3x − y)$cm

5cm

$(2x + 3y)$cm

5.

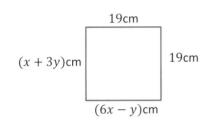

19cm

$(x + 3y)$cm

19cm

$(6x − y)$cm

6.

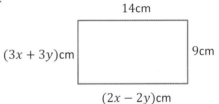

14cm

$(3x + 3y)$cm

9cm

$(2x − 2y)$cm

7.

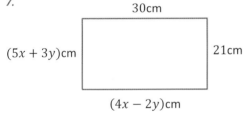

30cm

$(5x + 3y)$cm

21cm

$(4x − 2y)$cm

8.

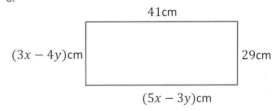

41cm

$(3x − 4y)$cm

29cm

$(5x − 3y)$cm

3.1 Simultaneous Equations Mixed Exercise

Exercise 3.1

Solve the following systems of equations by the most appropriate method:

1. $x + 2y = −1$
    $y = x − 2$

2. $y = 5x − 2$
    $y = 5 − 2x$

3. $2x + 3y = 9$
    $3x − 2y = 7$

4. $3x − 2y − 14 = 0$
    $2x + 3y − 5 = 0$

5. $3x − 2y − 8 = 0$
    $x − 3y = 5$

6. $4y = 2x − 14$
    $2x − 3y = 9$

7. $2x − 5y − 1 = 0$
    $x = 5y − 2$

8. $4x + 7y = 10$
    $2x + 3y = 4$

9. $y = 5 - 3x$
   $y = 5x - 11$

10. $x + 2y = 0$
    $3x + 5y - 2 = 0$

11. $3x + 2y + 1 = 0$
    $x - 5y = -23$

12. $3y = 4x - 17$
    $6y = 2 - 10x$

13. $6x + 4y + 6 = 0$
    $y = 5x - 8$

14. $y = 4x - 13$
    $y = x - 7$

15. $3x + 5y = 41$
    $5x + 3y = 31$

16. $x - 5y - 12 = 0$
    $3x + 4y + 2 = 0$

17. $5x = 3y + 11$
    $2y = 3x - 7$

18. $12x - 7y = 39$
    $5x - 4y = 13$

19. $5x + 3y + 1 = 0$
    $y = 4x - 6$

20. $2x + 3y + 2 = 0$
    $5x - 4y = 18$

21. $x + 2y = 5$
    $y = x - 3$

22. $y = 3x - 2$
    $y = 4 - 2x$

23. $5x + 3y = 2$
    $3x - 2y = 5$

24. $3x + 2y - 9 = 0$
    $2x + 3y - 3 = 0$

25. $3x - 5y - 8 = 0$
    $x - 2y = 3$

26. $5y = 2x - 14$
    $4x - 3y = 7$

27. $5x - 7y - 2 = 0$
    $x = 5y - 2$

28. $5x + 6y = 1$
    $2x + 3y = 4$

29. $y = 5 - x$
    $y = 5x - 3$

30. $x - 2y - 3 = 0$
    $2x + 3y - 2 = 0$

31. $2x + 2y + 1 = 0$
    $x - 5y = -2$

32. $y = 4x - 1$
    $y = 2 - 4x$

33. $x + 2y + 6 = 0$
    $y = x - 2$

34. $y = 4x - 2$
    $y = x - 7$

35. $2x + 5y = 4$
    $3x + 3y = 3$

36. $x - 5y - 1 = 0$
    $2x + y + 2 = 0$

37. $5x = 3y + 1$
    $2y = 3x - 7$

38. $x - 7y = 3$
    $3x - y = 3$

39. $5x + 3y + 1 = 0$
    $y = 2x - 5$

40. $2x + 3y + 2 = 0$
    $3x - 4y = 2$

Chapter 7
Changing the Subject of a Formula

2.1 Changing the Subject of the Form: $a = b + c$

The subject of a formula is the value that is on its own on one side of the formula (typically the left). For example, the subject of the formula $A = lb$ is A.

N.B. To change the subject of any formulae, perform the same method as solving equations, **i.e.** whatever operation is performed on one side of the equation, should also be performed on the other.

Worked Examples:

Change the subject in each of the following questions to c.

1. $a = b + c$	**2.** $b = c - d$	**3.** $x = y - c$
$(-b) \quad (-b)$	$(+d) \quad (+d)$	$(+c) \quad (+c)$
$a - b = c$	$b + d = c$	$c + x = y$
$c = a - b$	$c = b + d$	$(-x) \quad (-x)$
		$c = y - x$

Exercise 2.1

Change the subject of each question to the term given in square brackets:

1. $a = b + c$ [c]
2. $a = b + c$ [b]
3. $x = c + g$ [g]

4. $y = d - c$ [d]
5. $b = r + s$ [s]
6. $t = s - r$ [s]

7. $g = s + d$ [d]
8. $d = a - c$ [a]
9. $a = y - g$ [y]

10. $a = d - t$ [d]
11. $j = d + n$ [n]
12. $h = s + v$ [v]

13. $a = r - e$ [e]
14. $w = k + m$ [m]
15. $e = b - c$ [c]

16. $z = x + y$ [y]
17. $z = a + v$ [v]
18. $a = r - j$ [j]

19. $e = h + s$ [s]
20. $r = s - v$ [v]
21. $m = k - t$ [t]

22. $f = v - b$ [b]
23. $a = c + h$ [c]
24. $u = n - m$ [m]

2.2 Changing the Subject of the Form: $a = bc$

Worked Examples:

Change the subject in each of the following questions to c.

1. $a = bc$	**2.** $b = 2c$	**3.** $x = 5vc$
$(\div b) \quad (\div b)$	$(\div 2) \quad (\div 2)$	$(\div 5v) \quad (\div 5v)$
$\dfrac{a}{b} = c$	$\dfrac{b}{2} = c$	$\dfrac{x}{5v} = c$
$c = \dfrac{a}{b}$	$c = \dfrac{b}{2}$	$c = \dfrac{x}{5v}$

Exercise 2.2

Change the subject of each question to the term given in square brackets:

1. $a = bc$ $[c]$
2. $a = bc$ $[b]$
3. $x = cg$ $[g]$

4. $y = dc$ $[d]$
5. $b = rs$ $[s]$
6. $t = sr$ $[s]$

7. $g = sd$ $[d]$
8. $d = 4c$ $[c]$
9. $a = yg$ $[y]$

10. $a = 6t$ $[t]$
11. $j = 2n$ $[n]$
12. $h = 3v$ $[v]$

13. $a = 4e$ $[e]$
14. $w = 5m$ $[m]$
15. $e = bc$ $[c]$

16. $z = 3xy$ $[y]$
17. $z = 2bv$ $[v]$
18. $a = rj$ $[j]$

19. $e = 6s$ $[s]$
20. $r = sv$ $[v]$
21. $m = 2kt$ $[k]$

22. $f = 10cb$ $[c]$
23. $a = 8ch$ $[c]$
24. $u = 7nm$ $[n]$

2.3 Changing the Subject of the Form: $a = b/c$

Worked Examples:

Change the subject in each of the following questions to x.

1. $a = \dfrac{x}{b}$

  $x = ab$

2. $r = \dfrac{t}{x}$

  $xr = t$

  $x = \dfrac{t}{r}$

3. $r = \dfrac{2xb}{e}$

  $er = 2xb$

  $x = \dfrac{er}{2b}$

Exercise 2.3

Change the subject of each question to the term given in square brackets:

1. $a = \dfrac{c}{x}$ $[c]$
2. $d = \dfrac{b}{s}$ $[b]$
3. $h = \dfrac{g}{w}$ $[g]$

4. $n = \dfrac{d}{3}$ $[d]$
5. $e = \dfrac{s}{6}$ $[s]$
6. $w = \dfrac{e}{u}$ $[e]$

7. $q = \dfrac{d}{4a}$ $[d]$
8. $p = \dfrac{c}{2r}$ $[c]$
9. $b = \dfrac{y}{5u}$ $[y]$

10. $a = \dfrac{w}{t}$ $[t]$
11. $g = \dfrac{x}{n}$ $[n]$
12. $k = \dfrac{z}{v}$ $[v]$

13. $c = \dfrac{3x}{e}$ $[e]$
14. $j = \dfrac{2x}{m}$ $[m]$
15. $a = \dfrac{5t}{c}$ $[c]$

16. $c = \dfrac{2a}{b}$ $[a]$ 17. $m = \dfrac{4vx}{3d}$ $[v]$ 18. $t = \dfrac{3x}{2j}$ $[j]$

19. $a = \dfrac{5x}{4r}$ $[r]$ 20. $h = \dfrac{7ax}{3bc}$ $[b]$ 21. $s = \dfrac{5ux}{4rb}$ $[u]$

22. $y = \dfrac{2cd}{5ab}$ $[c]$ 23. $t = \dfrac{3bd}{4cg}$ $[d]$ 24. $c = \dfrac{xyz}{2ab}$ $[x]$

2.4 Changing the Subject of the Form: $a = b^c$

Worked Examples:

Change the subject in each of the following questions to c.

1. $a = c^2$ 2. $b = c^3$ 3. $x = \sqrt[3]{c}$
   $c = \sqrt{a}$ $c = \sqrt[3]{b}$ $c = x^3$

Exercise 2.4

Change the subject of each question to the term given in square brackets:

1. $a = b^2$ $[b]$ 2. $c = a^2$ $[a]$ 3. $x = g^3$ $[g]$

4. $y = d^4$ $[d]$ 5. $b = \sqrt{s}$ $[s]$ 6. $t = \sqrt{r}$ $[r]$

7. $g = \sqrt{d}$ $[d]$ 8. $d = c^5$ $[c]$ 9. $a = \sqrt[3]{y}$ $[y]$

10. $a = \sqrt[5]{t}$ $[t]$ 11. $j = \sqrt[7]{n}$ $[n]$ 12. $h = v^5$ $[v]$

13. $a = \sqrt{e}$ $[e]$ 14. $w = m^3$ $[m]$ 15. $e = \sqrt[6]{c}$ $[c]$

2.5 Changing the Subject Involving Two Operations

Worked Examples:

Change the subject in each of the following questions to x.

1. $y = mx + c$ 2. $r = 5x^2$ 3. $r = \dfrac{x+b}{e}$

   $y - c = mx$ $x^2 = \dfrac{r}{5}$ $er = x + b$

   $x = \dfrac{y-c}{m}$ $x = \sqrt{\dfrac{r}{5}}$ $x = er - b$

Exercise 2.5

Change the subject of each question to the term given in square brackets:

1. $y = mx + c$ $[m]$ 2. $d = 3x - u$ $[x]$ 3. $h = 5t + v$ $[t]$

4. $n = xb - r$ $[b]$ 5. $e = mn + b$ $[n]$ 6. $w = rt - xy$ $[r]$

7. $q = rg^2$ $[g]$ 8. $p = 6t^2$ $[t]$ 9. $b = 4g^3$ $[g]$

10. $a = \sqrt{6x}$ $[x]$ 11. $g = \sqrt[3]{3c}$ $[c]$ 12. $k = 6\sqrt{v}$ $[v]$

13. $c = (2e)^2$ $[e]$ 14. $j = \dfrac{x+a}{m}$ $[x]$ 15. $a = \dfrac{t-r}{h}$ $[t]$

16. $c = \dfrac{a-3b}{d}$ $[a]$ 17. $m = \dfrac{v-a}{d}$ $[v]$ 18. $t = \sqrt{\dfrac{x}{2}}$ $[x]$

19. $a = \dfrac{r^3}{4}$ $[r]$ 20. $h = \dfrac{b}{c} + r$ $[b]$ 21. $s = \dfrac{u}{2b} - g$ $[u]$

22. $y = \sqrt[3]{c} + e$ $[c]$ 23. $t = d^3 - u$ $[d]$ 24. $c = \sqrt[4]{x + 3e}$ $[x]$

2.6 Changing the Subject Involving Multiple Operations

Worked Examples:

Change the subject in each of the following questions to x.

1.
$$a = \sqrt{\frac{x-3e}{b}}$$
$$a^2 = \frac{x-3e}{b}$$
$$a^2 b = x - 3e$$
$$x = a^2 b + 3e$$

2.
$$r = \frac{t-x^2}{4a}$$
$$4ar = t - x^2$$
$$x^2 = t - 4ar$$
$$x = \sqrt{t - 4ar}$$

3.
$$b - x = cx + d$$
$$b = cx + x + d$$
$$b = x(c + 1) + d$$
$$b - d = x(c + 1)$$
$$x = \frac{b-d}{(c+1)}$$

Exercise 2.6

Change the subject of each question to the term given in square brackets:

1. $a = 3t^2 + b$ $[t]$ 2. $d = gr^3 - b$ $[r]$ 3. $h = \sqrt{\dfrac{g-2}{e}}$ $[g]$

4. $n = \sqrt[3]{\dfrac{d-b}{w}}$ $[d]$ 5. $e = \dfrac{s^2-m}{n}$ $[s]$ 6. $w = \dfrac{e^2-x}{r}$ $[e]$

7. $q = 4d^3 - 2e$ $[d]$ 8. $p = \dfrac{c}{2r^2}$ $[r]$ 9. $b = \dfrac{4y^3-d}{5u}$ $[y]$

10. $a + t = et$ $[t]$ 11. $g = \dfrac{n^2+w}{2r}$ $[n]$ 12. $k - v = rv$ $[v]$

13. $c = \dfrac{3x}{e} + a$ $[e]$

14. $j = \dfrac{2x}{m} - b$ $[m]$

15. $a = \sqrt[3]{\dfrac{e-b}{c}}$ $[c]$

16. $n = 3a^3 + m$ $[a]$

17. $m = 5\sqrt{v - 2b}$ $[v]$

18. $j + c = dj - t$ $[j]$

19. $p = \dfrac{r^2 - s}{de}$ $[r]$

20. $r = 4b^2 - d$ $[b]$

21. $k = \sqrt[3]{\dfrac{u-r}{v}}$ $[u]$

22. $b = 3\sqrt{v + 4e}$ $[v]$

23. $c = \dfrac{4r - e}{ay^3}$ $[y]$

24. $x + y = ax - m$ $[x]$

2.7 Changing the Subject of Common Formulae

Some common mathematical formulae are given below:

Volume of a Cylinder:	$V = \pi r^2 h$
Volume of a Cone:	$V = \dfrac{1}{3}\pi r^2 h$
Volume of a Sphere:	$V = \dfrac{4}{3}\pi r^3$
Surface area of a Sphere:	$A = 4\pi r^2$

In the formulae:
$'r'$ is the radius
$'h'$ is the height
$'\pi'$ is 'Pi' which is 3.14159 ...

Exercise 2.7

Change the subject of each question to the term given in square brackets:

1. $V = \pi r^2 h$ $[h]$

2. $V = \dfrac{1}{3}\pi r^2 h$ $[h]$

3. $V = \dfrac{4}{3}\pi r^3$ $[r]$

4. $A = 4\pi r^2$ $[r]$

5. $V = \pi r^2 h$ $[r]$

6. $V = \dfrac{1}{3}\pi r^2 h$ $[r]$

Chapter 8
Simplifying Expressions 2

2.1 Simplifying Basic Algebraic Fractions

When simplifying algebraic fractions, treat them like numerical fractions and cancel common factors on the numerator and denominator of the fraction.

Worked Examples:

1. $\dfrac{a}{2a} = \dfrac{a}{2a} = \dfrac{\cancel{a}}{2\cancel{a}} = \dfrac{1}{2}$

2. $abc \div ab = \dfrac{abc}{ab} = \dfrac{\cancel{ab}c}{\cancel{ab}} = c$

3. $\dfrac{6xy}{2y} = \dfrac{2\times3\times xy}{2y} = \dfrac{\cancel{2}\times3\times x\cancel{y}}{\cancel{2}\cancel{y}} = 3x$

4. $\dfrac{bc}{bc^2} = \dfrac{b\times c}{b\times c\times c} = \dfrac{\cancel{b}\times\cancel{c}}{\cancel{b}\times\cancel{c}\times c} = \dfrac{1}{c}$

Exercise 2.1

Simplify the following:

1. $\dfrac{a}{4a}$

2. $\dfrac{10b}{b}$

3. $\dfrac{8c}{c}$

4. $\dfrac{d}{5d}$

5. $\dfrac{e}{3e}$

6. $\dfrac{f}{2f}$

7. $\dfrac{8g}{g}$

8. $\dfrac{7h}{h}$

9. $\dfrac{8}{4r}$

10. $6h \div 2$

11. $\dfrac{5}{10j}$

12. $\dfrac{4m}{8}$

13. $3q \div q$

14. $\dfrac{2r}{10}$

15. $\dfrac{7}{14n}$

16. $\dfrac{a}{9a}$

17. $\dfrac{3b}{b}$

18. $\dfrac{2c}{8c}$

19. $\dfrac{d}{7d}$

20. $\dfrac{6e}{8e}$

21. $\dfrac{25f}{5f}$

22. $\dfrac{10g}{15g}$

23. $\dfrac{12h}{60h}$

24. $\dfrac{42r}{28r}$

25. $gk \div g$

26. $\dfrac{j}{jm}$

27. $\dfrac{mnp}{mn}$

28. $qrs \div qs$

29. $\dfrac{tw}{tvw}$

30. $\dfrac{z}{xyz}$

31. $8ab \div 10b$

32. $\dfrac{4b}{10bc}$

33. $\dfrac{28c}{14cd}$

34. $\dfrac{16de}{4def}$

35. $\dfrac{3gk}{12ghk}$

36. $\dfrac{5xy}{100y}$

37. $\dfrac{32abc}{24ac}$

38. $\dfrac{xy^2}{xy}$

39. $\dfrac{ab}{a^2b}$

40. $\dfrac{15bc^2}{25c}$

41. $\dfrac{18def}{27d^2e}$

42. $\dfrac{75ab^2c}{25ac^2}$

43. $\dfrac{27x^2y^2}{36xy^2}$

44. $\dfrac{60s^2tu^2}{72st^2u}$

45. $\dfrac{24mn^2}{42m^2n^2p}$

Algebraic fractions often need to be factorised before they can be simplified.

Worked Examples:

1. $\dfrac{4}{2a+2b} = \dfrac{2\times2}{2(a+b)} = \dfrac{\cancel{2}\times2}{\cancel{2}(a+b)} = \dfrac{2}{a+b}$

2. $\dfrac{10x-5}{15x} = \dfrac{5(2x-1)}{5\times3\times x} = \dfrac{\cancel{5}(2x-1)}{\cancel{5}\times3\times x} = \dfrac{2x-1}{3x}$

3. $\dfrac{2x-1}{8x^2-4x} = \dfrac{2x-1}{4x(2x-1)} = \dfrac{\cancel{2x-1}}{4x\cancel{(2x-1)}} = \dfrac{1}{4x}$

4. $\dfrac{6-r}{3r-18} = \dfrac{6-r}{-3(6-r)} = \dfrac{\cancel{6-r}}{-3\cancel{(6-r)}} = -\dfrac{1}{3}$

5. $\dfrac{x-3}{x^2-9} = \dfrac{x-3}{(x+3)(x-3)} = \dfrac{\cancel{x-3}}{(x+3)\cancel{(x-3)}} = \dfrac{1}{x+3}$

6. $\dfrac{x^2-3x+2}{x-1} = \dfrac{(x-2)(x-1)}{\cancel{x-1}} = x-2$

NB: When simplifying fractions, only *factors* of the numerator and denominator may be cancelled. In Example 2 there is an x left on both numerator and denominator. This is not a factor of the numerator (**i.e.** the remaining x does not multiply everything else on the numerator), so it should not be cancelled.

Exercise 2.2A

Simplify the following:

1. $\dfrac{5}{5a+5}$

2. $\dfrac{3a+6}{3}$

3. $\dfrac{2x-4}{2}$

4. $\dfrac{3}{12d-3}$

5. $\dfrac{4}{8e+12}$

6. $\dfrac{7}{14f-7}$

7. $\dfrac{6g-12}{3}$

8. $\dfrac{7h-21}{7}$

9. $\dfrac{10}{4j-2k}$

10. $\dfrac{6}{4k-12m}$

11. $\dfrac{8m-10}{20}$

12. $\dfrac{12n-3}{6}$

13. $\dfrac{5n}{20n-10}$

14. $\dfrac{6p}{10p-4}$

15. $\dfrac{12n}{14n-6}$

16. $\dfrac{9a-12}{6a}$

17. $\dfrac{b-2}{b^2-2b}$

18. $\dfrac{c+5}{c^2+5c}$

19. $\dfrac{2d^2-8d}{d-4}$

20. $\dfrac{5e^2+15e}{e+3}$

21. $\dfrac{f+5}{f^2-25}$

22. $\dfrac{g^2-1}{g+1}$

23. $\dfrac{h-4}{h^2-16}$

24. $\dfrac{9-r}{81-r^2}$

25. $\dfrac{x-1}{x^2-5x+4}$

26. $\dfrac{x^2+x-6}{(x+3)(x+1)}$

27. $\dfrac{(y-5)(y+9)}{5y^2-25y}$

28. $\dfrac{32h-16}{40h}$

29. $\dfrac{25z}{100z-35}$

30. $\dfrac{5-x}{3x-15}$

31. $\dfrac{x+7}{x^2+2x-35}$

32. $\dfrac{6b^2+18b}{b+3}$

33. $\dfrac{x^2+5x+6}{(x+2)(x+5)}$

34. $\dfrac{(y+9)(y+3)}{y^2-81}$

35. $\dfrac{8-s}{5s-40}$

36. $\dfrac{(2x-1)(x+6)}{2x^2-7x+3}$

Worked Examples:

1. $\dfrac{x^2+3x}{x^2-9} = \dfrac{x(x+3)}{(x-3)(x+3)} = \dfrac{x\cancel{(x+3)}}{(x-3)\cancel{(x+3)}} = \dfrac{x}{x-3}$

2. $\dfrac{x^2-3x+2}{x^2+3x-4} = \dfrac{(x-2)(x-1)}{(x+4)(x-1)} = \dfrac{(x-2)\cancel{(x-1)}}{(x+4)\cancel{(x-1)}} = \dfrac{x-2}{x+4}$

Exercise 2.2B

Simplify the following:

1. $\dfrac{x^2-6x}{x^2-36}$

2. $\dfrac{x^2-1}{x^2-2x+1}$

3. $\dfrac{x^2+3x}{x^2-x-12}$

4. $\dfrac{x^2-16}{x^2+4x}$

5. $\dfrac{x^2-3x-10}{x^2-4}$

6. $\dfrac{x^2-64}{x^2+8x}$

7. $\dfrac{x^2-7x+12}{x^2-9}$

8. $\dfrac{x^2-x-12}{x^2+3x}$

9. $\dfrac{x^2+6x+9}{x^2-9}$

10. $\dfrac{x^2+10x+25}{x^2+5x}$

11. $\dfrac{x^2+x}{x^2-1}$

12. $\dfrac{6x-12}{x^2-4x+4}$

13. $\dfrac{x^2-3x-4}{4x+4}$

14. $\dfrac{x^2-2x}{7x-14}$

15. $\dfrac{x^2+5x+6}{x^2+4x+4}$

16. $\dfrac{x^2-11x+10}{x^2+2x-3}$

17. $\dfrac{x^2-14x+40}{x^2-100}$

18. $\dfrac{x^2+7x-18}{x^2-10x+16}$

19. $\dfrac{2x^2-3x-9}{x^2-9}$

20. $\dfrac{x^2-6x+8}{3x^2-10x+8}$

21. $\dfrac{14+5x-x^2}{49-x^2}$

22. $\dfrac{2x^2+x-6}{2x^2-8}$

23. $\dfrac{12+x-x^2}{48-3x^2}$

24. $\dfrac{5-9x-2x^2}{100-4x^2}$

2.3 Multiplication of Algebraic Fractions

When multiplying algebraic fractions, follow the same process as numerical fractions. The numerator multiplies the numerator and the denominator multiplies the denominator.

Worked Examples:

1. $\dfrac{x}{y} \times \dfrac{x}{z} = \dfrac{x^2}{yz}$

2. $\dfrac{a}{b} \times \dfrac{b}{c} = \dfrac{a}{\cancel{b}} \times \dfrac{\cancel{b}}{c} = \dfrac{a}{c}$

> **NB:** When multiplying fractions, it is a good idea to simplify before multiplying, as in examples 2-4.

3. $\dfrac{4x}{3yz} \times \dfrac{5z}{2x} = \dfrac{2\times2\times x}{3yz} \times \dfrac{5z}{2x} = \dfrac{\cancel{2}\times2\times\cancel{x}}{3y\cancel{z}} \times \dfrac{5\cancel{z}}{\cancel{2}\cancel{x}} = \dfrac{10}{3y}$

4. $\dfrac{4mn}{10p} \times \dfrac{5p^2}{6n^2} = \dfrac{2\times2\times m\times n}{3\times5\times p} \times \dfrac{5\times p\times p}{2\times3\times n\times n} = \dfrac{\cancel{2}\times2\times m\times\cancel{n}}{3\times\cancel{5}\times\cancel{p}} \times \dfrac{\cancel{5}\times p\times\cancel{p}}{2\times3\times\cancel{n}\times n} = \dfrac{2mp}{9n}$

Exercise 2.3

Multiply the following fractions, giving your answer in its simplest form:

1. $\dfrac{a}{b} \times \dfrac{c}{d}$

2. $\dfrac{c}{d} \times \dfrac{e}{f}$

3. $\dfrac{g}{h} \times \dfrac{g}{k}$

4. $\dfrac{s}{t} \times \dfrac{u}{t}$

5. $\dfrac{x}{y} \times \dfrac{z}{x}$

6. $\dfrac{a}{b} \times \dfrac{b}{c}$

7. $\dfrac{a^2}{b} \times \dfrac{b}{a}$

8. $\dfrac{n}{m^2} \times \dfrac{m}{n^2}$

9. $\dfrac{u^2}{y} \times \dfrac{z}{u}$

10. $\dfrac{v}{b} \times \dfrac{b}{v^2}$

11. $\dfrac{t^2}{d^2} \times \dfrac{d}{t}$

12. $\dfrac{k}{b^2} \times \dfrac{b}{k^2}$

13. $\dfrac{4c}{d} \times \dfrac{d}{2c}$

14. $\dfrac{3e}{v} \times \dfrac{v}{12e}$

15. $\dfrac{2n^2}{15r} \times \dfrac{5r}{n}$

16. $\dfrac{3c}{10b} \times \dfrac{20b}{c^2}$

17. $\dfrac{4s}{t} \times \dfrac{t}{2u}$

18. $\dfrac{3s}{r} \times \dfrac{r}{6t}$

19. $\dfrac{3c}{10b} \times \dfrac{5c}{9d}$

20. $\dfrac{c}{10b} \times \dfrac{5b}{c}$

21. $\dfrac{8a}{9b} \times \dfrac{21a}{10c}$

22. $\dfrac{6c}{5d} \times \dfrac{10c}{18d}$

23. $\dfrac{3a}{4b} \times \dfrac{4b}{5c}$

24. $\dfrac{6x}{7y} \times \dfrac{z}{3x}$

25. $\dfrac{2r^2}{3s} \times \dfrac{t}{4r}$

26. $\dfrac{2v}{3u^2} \times \dfrac{uv}{6w}$

27. $\dfrac{2e}{7g} \times \dfrac{14f}{e^2}$

28. $\dfrac{xy^2}{3z} \times \dfrac{12x}{zy}$

29. $\dfrac{24ab}{35c} \times \dfrac{7ac}{6b}$

30. $\dfrac{15vw}{16x} \times \dfrac{24wx}{5v}$

31. $\dfrac{8s^2w}{21u} \times \dfrac{3uv}{2st}$

32. $\dfrac{20x^2}{27yz} \times \dfrac{3xz}{8y}$

33. $\dfrac{bc^2}{16d^2} \times \dfrac{48d}{7bc}$

34. $\dfrac{9w^2}{vu^2} \times \dfrac{u^2}{27vw^2}$

35. $\dfrac{25z^2}{28xy^2} \times \dfrac{7y}{30xz^2}$

36. $\dfrac{24y^2}{v^2} \times \dfrac{v^2}{27xy^2}$

2.4 Division of Algebraic Fractions

When dividing algebraic fractions, follow the same process as numerical fractions. Turn the second fraction upside down and multiply the fractions.

Worked Examples:

1. $\dfrac{x}{y} \div \dfrac{x}{z} = \dfrac{x}{y} \times \dfrac{z}{x} = \dfrac{\cancel{x}}{y} \times \dfrac{z}{\cancel{x}} = \dfrac{z}{y}$

2. $\dfrac{4x}{3yz} \div \dfrac{2x}{5z} = \dfrac{2 \times 2 \times x}{3yz} \times \dfrac{5z}{2x} = \dfrac{\cancel{2} \times 2 \times \cancel{x}}{3y\cancel{z}} \times \dfrac{5\cancel{z}}{\cancel{2x}} = \dfrac{10}{3y}$

3. $\dfrac{5}{x^2-3x-18} \div \dfrac{15}{x-6} = \dfrac{5}{(x-6)(x+3)} \times \dfrac{x-6}{5 \times 3} = \dfrac{\cancel{5}}{(\cancel{x-6})(x+3)} \times \dfrac{\cancel{x-6}}{\cancel{5} \times 3} = \dfrac{1}{x+3} \times \dfrac{1}{3} = \dfrac{1}{3x+9}$

NB: It may be necessary to factorise and simplify fractions before division, as in example 3.

Exercise 2.4

Divide the following fractions, giving your answer in its simplest form:

1. $\dfrac{a}{b} \div \dfrac{c}{d}$

2. $\dfrac{c}{d} \div \dfrac{e}{f}$

3. $\dfrac{g}{h} \div \dfrac{g}{k}$

4. $\dfrac{s}{t} \div \dfrac{u}{t}$

5. $\dfrac{x}{y} \div \dfrac{x}{z}$

6. $\dfrac{a}{b} \div \dfrac{a}{b}$

7. $\dfrac{a^2}{b} \div \dfrac{a}{c}$

8. $\dfrac{n}{m^2} \div \dfrac{n^2}{m}$

9. $\dfrac{u^2}{y} \div \dfrac{u}{z}$

10. $\dfrac{v}{b} \div \dfrac{v^2}{b}$

11. $\dfrac{t^2}{d^2} \div \dfrac{t}{d}$

12. $\dfrac{k}{b^2} \div \dfrac{k^2}{b}$

13. $\dfrac{8c}{d} \div \dfrac{2c}{d}$

14. $\dfrac{4e}{r} \div \dfrac{12e}{r}$

15. $\dfrac{2n^2}{25r} \div \dfrac{n}{10r}$

16. $\dfrac{3c}{10b} \div \dfrac{6}{5b}$

17. $\dfrac{4s}{t} \div \dfrac{12t}{u}$

18. $\dfrac{3s}{r} \div \dfrac{18}{5r}$

19. $\dfrac{3c}{10b} \div \dfrac{9a}{20e}$

20. $\dfrac{6c}{10b} \div \dfrac{5d}{9b}$

21. $\dfrac{7a}{9b} \div \dfrac{21a}{27c}$

22. $\dfrac{12c}{5d} \div \dfrac{24c^2}{25d}$

23. $\dfrac{3a^2}{4b} \div \dfrac{9a}{16b}$

24. $\dfrac{6x^2}{7y} \div \dfrac{9x}{21y^2}$

25. $\dfrac{6r^2}{3s} \div \dfrac{14r}{15st}$

26. $\dfrac{12v}{7u^2} \div \dfrac{3w}{14uv}$

27. $\dfrac{5e}{30g} \div \dfrac{25e}{8g^2}$

28. $\dfrac{xy^2}{3z} \div \dfrac{15y}{18x}$

29. $\dfrac{x^2+x}{8} \div \dfrac{x}{4}$

30. $\dfrac{x^2-4}{5x} \div \dfrac{x+2}{10}$

31. $\dfrac{4x^2+8x}{3} \div \dfrac{x}{12}$

32. $\dfrac{5}{x^2-9} \div \dfrac{x+1}{x-3}$

33. $\dfrac{x^2+2x+1}{10} \div \dfrac{x+1}{5}$

34. $\dfrac{x}{x^2-3x+2} \div \dfrac{x}{x-2}$

35. $\dfrac{9}{x^2+x-12} \div \dfrac{18}{x-3}$

36. $\dfrac{x^2+x}{x^2-1} \div \dfrac{x}{x-1}$

2.5 Addition/Subtraction of Algebraic Fractions

When adding or subtracting algebraic fractions, a *common denominator* is needed. It is best to find the lowest common denominator.

Worked Examples:

1. $\dfrac{3}{a} + \dfrac{b}{a} = \dfrac{3+b}{a}$

2. $\dfrac{4}{b} - \dfrac{5}{a} = \dfrac{4a}{ab} - \dfrac{5b}{ab} = \dfrac{4a-5b}{ab}$

NB: In example 2, the lowest common denominator is ab. In order to find each numerator, consider what the denominator has been multiplied by. Once the fractions have the same denominator, they can be added or subtracted.

3. $\dfrac{5}{a^2} + \dfrac{3}{2a} = \dfrac{5\times2}{2a^2} + \dfrac{3\times a}{2a^2} = \dfrac{10+3a}{2a^2}$

Exercise 2.5A

Add or subtract the following fractions, giving your answer in its simplest form:

1. $\dfrac{3}{b}+\dfrac{4}{b}$

2. $\dfrac{5}{d}+\dfrac{6}{d}$

3. $\dfrac{3}{a}+\dfrac{g}{a}$

4. $\dfrac{7}{t}+\dfrac{u}{t}$

5. $\dfrac{7}{y}-\dfrac{4}{y}$

6. $\dfrac{6}{b}-\dfrac{2}{b}$

7. $\dfrac{6}{c}-\dfrac{a}{c}$

8. $\dfrac{t}{m}-\dfrac{n}{m}$

9. $\dfrac{3}{y}+\dfrac{2}{z}$

10. $\dfrac{4}{b}-\dfrac{1}{c}$

11. $\dfrac{2}{d}+\dfrac{4}{e}$

12. $\dfrac{1}{c}-\dfrac{3}{b}$

13. $\dfrac{8}{d^2}+\dfrac{2c}{d}$

14. $\dfrac{4}{r^2}-\dfrac{1}{r}$

15. $\dfrac{3}{c}+\dfrac{2}{c^2}$

16. $\dfrac{3}{b^2}-\dfrac{1}{2b}$

17. $\dfrac{3}{2t}+\dfrac{1}{3u}$

18. $\dfrac{3}{4r}-\dfrac{3}{5t}$

19. $\dfrac{7}{b}+\dfrac{8}{9c}$

20. $\dfrac{3}{4a}-\dfrac{5}{6b}$

21. $\dfrac{2a}{9b}+\dfrac{4a}{3c}$

22. $\dfrac{c}{5d^2}-\dfrac{6}{d}$

23. $\dfrac{3a}{4b^3}+\dfrac{9a}{b}$

24. $\dfrac{6x^2}{7y}-\dfrac{9x}{21y^2}$

25. $\dfrac{9}{15s^2}+\dfrac{11t}{3s}$

26. $\dfrac{11}{12r}-\dfrac{4}{15s}$

27. $\dfrac{4}{6g}+\dfrac{3a}{8e}$

28. $\dfrac{3b}{8z}-\dfrac{c}{12x}$

29. $\dfrac{5}{ab}+\dfrac{2d}{bc}$

30. $\dfrac{5}{xy}-\dfrac{3w}{yz}$

31. $\dfrac{2t}{rs}+\dfrac{3r}{st}$

32. $\dfrac{5}{cd^2}-\dfrac{c}{de}$

Worked Examples:

1. $\dfrac{5}{x-2}+\dfrac{3}{x}=\dfrac{5x}{x(x-2)}+\dfrac{3(x-2)}{x(x-2)}=\dfrac{5x+3x-6}{x(x-2)}=\dfrac{8x-6}{x(x-2)}$

2. $\dfrac{6}{x-5}+\dfrac{5}{x+6}=\dfrac{6(x+6)}{(x-5)(x+6)}+\dfrac{5(x-5)}{(x-5)(x+6)}=\dfrac{6x+36+5x-25}{(x-5)(x+6)}=\dfrac{11x+11}{(x-5)(x+6)}$

3. $\dfrac{2}{x-3}-\dfrac{4}{x-5}=\dfrac{2(x-5)}{(x-3)(x-5)}-\dfrac{4(x-3)}{(x-3)(x-5)}=\dfrac{2x-10-4x+12}{(x-3)(x-5)}=\dfrac{2-2x}{(x-3)(x-5)}$

NB: Be careful with signs when subtracting negative terms (as in example 3).

Exercise 2.5B

Add or subtract the following fractions, giving your answer in its simplest form:

1. $\dfrac{3}{x-1}+\dfrac{4}{x}$

2. $\dfrac{5}{x}+\dfrac{6}{x+3}$

3. $\dfrac{x+1}{3}+\dfrac{x}{2}$

4. $\dfrac{7}{x-4}+\dfrac{2}{x}$

5. $\dfrac{x-2}{3}-\dfrac{x}{4}$

6. $\dfrac{6}{x+5}-\dfrac{2}{x}$

7. $\dfrac{1}{x}-\dfrac{5}{x-3}$

8. $\dfrac{3}{x-5}-\dfrac{2}{x}$

9. $\dfrac{3}{x-1} + \dfrac{2}{x-2}$

10. $\dfrac{4}{x+2} - \dfrac{1}{x+5}$

11. $\dfrac{x+3}{4} + \dfrac{x-2}{2}$

12. $\dfrac{x-3}{5} - \dfrac{x-5}{4}$

13. $\dfrac{2}{x+5} + \dfrac{3}{x-5}$

14. $\dfrac{4}{x-1} - \dfrac{1}{x+1}$

15. $\dfrac{3}{x-4} + \dfrac{2}{x+4}$

16. $\dfrac{3}{x+3} - \dfrac{1}{x-3}$

17. $\dfrac{x+2}{4} + \dfrac{x+3}{3}$

18. $\dfrac{3}{x-3} - \dfrac{5}{x-5}$

19. $\dfrac{7}{x-2} + \dfrac{8}{x+9}$

20. $\dfrac{x+5}{4} - \dfrac{x-2}{6}$

21. $\dfrac{3}{x^2-1} + \dfrac{4}{x+1}$

22. $\dfrac{1}{x^2-4} - \dfrac{3}{x-2}$

23. $\dfrac{3}{x^2-9} + \dfrac{2}{x-3}$

24. $\dfrac{6}{x+5} - \dfrac{2}{x^2-25}$

Chapter 9
Completing the Square

Completing the square is the process of taking a trinomial expression (usually one that does not factorise) and turning it in to a perfect square trinomial (**see chapter 2 exercise 2.4, page 17**) with something added on or taken away. This form is useful for finding the turning point of a quadratic function. It can be expressed generally in the following way:

$$ax^2 + bx + c = a\left(x + \frac{b}{2a}\right)^2 + c - \left(\frac{b}{2a}\right)^2$$

This may look quite complicated, but the following illustration may help.

We can find the area of the shape on the left, by considering its component parts, or by considering the shape on the right, less the missing part.

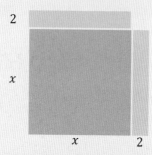

The area of the shape on the left is $x^2 + 2x + 2x = x^2 + 4x$.

The area of the shape on the right can be written as $(x + 2)^2 = x^2 + 4x + 4$.

To find the area of the shape on the left in terms of the area on the right, it can be written as the whole square, less the missing part,

i.e. $x^2 + 4x + 4 - 4 = (x + 2)^2 - 4$.

This is called completing the square.

Worked Examples:

1. $x^2 + 4x + 7$
$= (x^2 + 4x) + 7$
$= (x + 2)^2 + 7 - 2^2$
$= (x + 2)^2 + 7 - 4$
$= (x + 2)^2 + 3$

2. $x^2 - 6x + 10$
$= (x^2 - 6x) + 10$
$= (x - 3)^2 + 10 - (-3)^2$
$= (x - 3)^2 + 10 - 9$
$= (x - 3)^2 + 1$

3. $x^2 - 10x + 30$
$= (x^2 - 10x) + 30$
$= (x - 5)^2 + 30 - (-5)^2$
$= (x - 5)^2 + 30 - 25$
$= (x - 5)^2 + 5$

NB: In line 3 of each example, the coefficient of the x term is halved inside the bracket, then squared and taken away outside the bracket.

Exercise 2.1

Complete the square of the following:

1. $x^2 + 2x + 3$

2. $x^2 - 2x + 4$

3. $x^2 - 4x + 5$

4. $x^2 - 4x + 6$

5. $x^2 - 6x + 10$

6. $x^2 + 4x + 10$

7. $x^2 - 6x + 12$

8. $x^2 + 10x + 30$

9. $x^2 - 8x + 25$

10. $x^2 + 10x + 27$

11. $x^2 - 6x - 2$

12. $x^2 - 12x + 7$

13. $x^2 + 16x - 7$

14. $x^2 - 8x - 4$

15. $x^2 - 10x + 5$

16. $x^2 + 16x + 32$

17. $x^2 - 18x + 5$

18. $x^2 + 20x + 3$

19. $x^2 + 30x - 6$

20. $x^2 + 22x - 21$

21. $x^2 - 16x - 12$

22. $x^2 + 12x - 14$

23. $x^2 - 16x - 27$

24. $x^2 + 20x + 10$

25. $x^2 - 40x - 35$

26. $x^2 - 30x - 25$

27. $x^2 + 8x - 6$

28. $x^2 + 18x - 12$

29. $x^2 - 14x - 16$

30. $x^2 - 30x - 24$

3.1 Completing the Square – Involving Fractions

Worked Examples:

1. $x^2 + 3x + 7$
$= (x^2 + 3x) + 7$
$= \left(x + \frac{3}{2}\right)^2 + 7 - \left(\frac{3}{2}\right)^2$
$= \left(x + \frac{3}{2}\right)^2 + 7 - \frac{9}{4}$
$= \left(x + \frac{3}{2}\right)^2 + \frac{28}{4} - \frac{9}{4}$
$= \left(x + \frac{3}{2}\right)^2 + \frac{19}{4}$

2. $x^2 - 5x + 9$
$= (x^2 - 5x) + 9$
$= \left(x - \frac{5}{2}\right)^2 + 9 - \left(-\frac{5}{2}\right)^2$
$= \left(x - \frac{5}{2}\right)^2 + 9 - \frac{25}{4}$
$= \left(x - \frac{5}{2}\right)^2 + \frac{36}{4} - \frac{25}{4}$
$= \left(x - \frac{5}{2}\right)^2 + \frac{11}{4}$

3. $x^2 - 11x + 32$
$= (x^2 - 11x) + 32$
$= \left(x - \frac{11}{2}\right)^2 + 32 - \left(-\frac{11}{2}\right)^2$
$= \left(x - \frac{11}{2}\right)^2 + 32 - \frac{121}{4}$
$= \left(x - \frac{11}{2}\right)^2 + \frac{128}{4} - \frac{121}{4}$
$= \left(x - \frac{11}{2}\right)^2 + \frac{7}{4}$

Exercise 3.1

Complete the square of the following:

1. $x^2 + 3x + 3$

2. $x^2 - 5x + 8$

3. $x^2 - 7x + 5$

4. $x^2 - 5x + 6$

5. $x^2 - 3x + 10$

6. $x^2 + 9x + 10$

7. $x^2 - 7x + 11$

8. $x^2 + 9x + 30$

9. $x^2 - 7x + 25$

10. $x^2 + x + 27$

11. $x^2 - 11x - 2$

12. $x^2 - x + 7$

13. $x^2 + 9x - 7$

14. $x^2 - 11x - 4$

15. $x^2 - 13x + 5$

16. $x^2 + 7x + 32$

17. $x^2 - 5x + 5$

18. $x^2 + 7x + 3$

19. $x^2 + 13x - 6$

20. $x^2 + 15x - 21$

21. $x^2 - 11x - 11$

22. $x^2 + 15x - 14$

23. $x^2 - 5x - 27$

24. $x^2 + 3x + 9$

25. $x^2 - 5x - 35$

26. $x^2 - 7x - 25$

27. $x^2 + 9x - 6$

28. $x^2 + 3x - 14$

29. $x^2 - 11x - 16$

30. $x^2 - 5x - 23$

Worked Examples:

1. $2x^2 + 8x + 9$

$= (2x^2 + 8x) + 9$

$= 2(x^2 + 4x) + 9$

$= 2(x + 2)^2 + 9 - 2(2)^2$

$= 2(x + 2)^2 + 9 - 8$

$= 2(x + 2)^2 + 1$

2. $3x^2 - 24x + 25$

$= (3x^2 - 24x) + 25$

$= 3(x^2 - 8x) + 25$

$= 3(x - 4)^2 + 25 - 3(-4)^2$

$= 3(x - 4)^2 + 25 - 48$

$= 3(x - 4)^2 - 23$

3. $5x^2 - 5x + 28$

$= (5x^2 - 5x) + 28$

$= 5(x^2 - x) + 28$

$= 5\left(x - \frac{1}{2}\right)^2 + 28 - 5\left(-\frac{1}{2}\right)^2$

$= 5\left(x - \frac{1}{2}\right)^2 + 28 - \frac{5}{4}$

$= 5\left(x - \frac{1}{2}\right)^2 + \frac{107}{4}$

Exercise 3.2

Complete the square of the following:

1. $2x^2 + 6x + 9$

2. $2x^2 - 8x + 7$

3. $3x^2 - 6x + 5$

4. $4x^2 - 8x + 11$

5. $3x^2 - 12x + 16$

6. $4x^2 + 16x + 19$

7. $3x^2 - 24x + 31$

8. $2x^2 + 12x + 33$

9. $4x^2 - 8x + 25$

10. $7x^2 + 14x + 29$

11. $6x^2 - 12x - 2$

12. $9x^2 - 18x + 71$

13. $12x^2 + 36x - 1$

14. $20x^2 - 40x - 4$

15. $6x^2 - 24x + 59$

16. $3x^2 + 9x + 31$

17. $2x^2 - 6x + 5$

18. $4x^2 + 12x + 17$

19. $6x^2 + 18x - 6$

20. $5x^2 + 15x - 1$

21. $8x^2 - 24x - 13$

22. $2x^2 + 10x - 1$

23. $3x^2 - 21x - 29$

24. $4x^2 + 20x + 11$

25. $8x^2 - 40x - 35$

26. $10x^2 - 30x - 23$

27. $7x^2 + 35x - 6$

28. $11x^2 + 33x - 14$

29. $9x^2 - 27x - 38$

30. $6x^2 - 42x - 25$

3.3 Completing the Square – Negative Squared Term

Worked Examples:

1. $5 - 4x - x^2$

$= -x^2 - 4x + 5$

$= -(x^2 + 4x) + 5$

$= -(x + 2)^2 + 5 - (-1)(2)^2$

$= -(x + 2)^2 + 5 + 4$

$= -(x + 2)^2 + 9$

2. $1 + 3x - x^2$

$= -x^2 + 3x + 1$

$= -(x^2 - 3x) + 1$

$= -\left(x - \frac{3}{2}\right)^2 + 1 - (-1)\left(-\frac{3}{2}\right)^2$

$= -(x - 3)^2 + 1 + \frac{9}{4}$

$= -(x - 3)^2 + \frac{13}{4}$

3. $2 - 9x - 3x^2$

$= -3x^2 - 9x + 2$

$= -3(x^2 + 3x) + 5$

$= -3\left(x + \frac{3}{2}\right)^2 + 5 - (-3)\left(\frac{3}{2}\right)^2$

$= -3\left(x + \frac{3}{2}\right)^2 + 5 + \frac{27}{4}$

$= -3\left(x + \frac{3}{2}\right)^2 + \frac{47}{4}$

Exercise 3.3

Complete the square of the following:

1. $4 - 2x - x^2$

2. $7 - 4x - x^2$

3. $1 + 2x - x^2$

4. $7 - 2x - x^2$

5. $1 + 6x - x^2$

6. $2 - 2x - x^2$

7. $6 + 4x - x^2$

8. $5 + 6x - x^2$

9. $5 - 6x - x^2$

10. $7 - 8x - x^2$

11. $5 + 10x - x^2$

12. $13 - 6x - x^2$

13. $2 + 10x - x^2$

14. $17 - 12x - x^2$

15. $4 + 14x - x^2$

16. $3 - 4x - 2x^2$

17. $1 - 3x - x^2$

18. $11 + 5x - x^2$

19. $1 - 6x - 3x^2$

20. $5 + 4x - 2x^2$

21. $4 + 12x - 3x^2$

22. $5 - 9x - 3x^2$

23. $11 - 6x - 2x^2$

24. $11 + 12x - 4x^2$

25. $2 + 5x - 5x^2$

26. $5 - 4x - 4x^2$

27. $3 - 10x - 2x^2$

28. $5 + 12x - 4x^2$

29. $13 - 6x - 2x^2$

30. $1 + 25x - 5x^2$

Chapter 10
Solving Equations 3 – Quadratic Equations

2.1 Solving Quadratic Equations

The diagram on the right represents a graph of a quadratic function. This graph is commonly called a **parabola**. To solve a quadratic function is to find the x-coordinates at which the graph of the quadratic function is equal to zero, **i.e.** where the graph intersects the x-axis. These values are known as the **solutions**, the **roots** or the **zeros** of a quadratic function.

In the diagram, the roots are $x = -2$ and $x = 2$.

When solving a quadratic function, such as $y = x^2 - 6x - 16$, the quadratic function needs to be *equated to zero*. This is because any line or curve intersects the x-axis when $y = 0$.

Worked Examples:

Solve the following quadratic equations:

1. $x(x + 4) = 0$

$x = 0$ *or* $x + 4 = 0$

$x = 0$ $x = -4$

2. $2x(x - 2) = 0$

$2x = 0$ *or* $x - 2 = 0$

$x = 0$ $x = 2$

3. $-3x(3x - 4) = 0$

$-3x = 0$ *or* $3x - 4 = 0$

$x = 0$ $x = \dfrac{4}{3}$

Exercise 2.1A

Solve the following quadratic equations:

1. $x(x - 1) = 0$

2. $x(x + 2) = 0$

3. $x(x + 1) = 0$

4. $x(x - 2) = 0$

5. $x(x + 3) = 0$

6. $x(x + 5) = 0$

7. $x(x + 6) = 0$

8. $2x(x - 9) = 0$

9. $3x(x + 5) = 0$

10. $2x(x + 1) = 0$

11. $x(3x - 5) = 0$

12. $x(2x + 3) = 0$

13. $x(2x + 1) = 0$

14. $2x(3x + 2) = 0$

15. $5x(7x + 3) = 0$

16. $-2x(5x + 1) = 0$

17. $-3x(2x - 1) = 0$

18. $-x(9x + 2) = 0$

Worked Examples:

Solve the following quadratic equations:

1. $(x - 2)(x + 5) = 0$

$x - 2 = 0$ *or* $x + 5 = 0$

$x = 2$ $x = -5$

2. $(x + 1)(2x - 1) = 0$

$x + 1 = 0$ *or* $2x - 1 = 0$

$x = -1$ $x = \dfrac{1}{2}$

3. $(2x + 3)(x - 4) = 0$

$2x + 3 = 0$ *or* $x - 4 = 0$

$x = -\dfrac{3}{2}$ $x = 4$

Exercise 2.1B

Solve the following quadratic equations:

1. $(x - 5)(x - 2) = 0$

2. $(x - 4)(x - 1) = 0$

3. $(x + 3)(x - 4) = 0$

4. $(x + 7)(x + 1) = 0$

5. $(x + 6)(x + 3) = 0$

6. $(x - 9)(x + 1) = 0$

7. $(x + 4)(x - 3) = 0$

8. $(x + 5)(x - 3) = 0$

9. $(x + 2)(x - 2) = 0$

10. $(x - 5)(x - 1) = 0$

11. $(x - 3)(x + 9) = 0$

12. $(x + 8)(x - 1) = 0$

13. $(3x - 2)(x + 3) = 0$

14. $(4x - 3)(x - 1) = 0$

15. $(4x + 3)(x + 2) = 0$

16. $(x - 2)(2x + 3) = 0$

17. $(2x - 3)(x + 2) = 0$

18. $(2x + 5)(x - 1) = 0$

19. $(x - 7)(x + 9) = 0$

20. $(2x + 1)(x - 3) = 0$

21. $(2x - 3)(x + 2) = 0$

22. $(2x + 5)(x + 9) = 0$

23. $(2x + 5)(2x - 1) = 0$

24. $(3x + 2)(2x - 3) = 0$

2.2 Solving Quadratics by Factorising

Often quadratic equations need to be factorised (see **chapter 3**) before they can be solved.

Worked Examples:

Solve the following quadratic equations:

1. $x^2 - 3x = 0$
    $x(x - 3) = 0$
    $x = 0$ or $x - 3 = 0$
    $x = 0$ or $x = 3$

2. $x^2 - 9 = 0$
    $(x + 3)(x - 3) = 0$
    $x + 3 = 0$ or $x - 3 = 0$
    $x = -3$ or $x = 3$

3. $x^2 - 6x - 16 = 0$
    $(x + 2)(x - 8) = 0$
    $x + 2 = 0$ or $x - 8 = 0$
    $x = -2$ or $x = 8$

Exercise 2.2A

Solve the following quadratic equations by factorising:

1. $x^2 + 5x = 0$

2. $x^2 - 4x = 0$

3. $x^2 + 7x = 0$

4. $x^2 + 2x = 0$

5. $x^2 - 5x = 0$

6. $x^2 - 10x = 0$

7. $x^2 + 6x = 0$

8. $x^2 + 3x = 0$

9. $x^2 - x = 0$

10. $2x^2 + 8x = 0$

11. $3x^2 - 15x = 0$

12. $5x^2 + 10x = 0$

13. $4x^2 - 12x = 0$

14. $4x^2 - 100x = 0$

15. $3x^2 - 27x = 0$

16. $5x^2 - 60x = 0$

17. $200x - 4x^2 = 0$

18. $9x^2 - 36x = 0$

Exercise 2.2B

Solve the following quadratics equations by factorising:

1. $x^2 - 1 = 0$
2. $x^2 - 9 = 0$
3. $x^2 - 4 = 0$
4. $x^2 - 16 = 0$
5. $x^2 - 25 = 0$
6. $x^2 - 36 = 0$
7. $x^2 - 49 = 0$
8. $x^2 - 81 = 0$
9. $x^2 - 100 = 0$
10. $2x^2 - 2 = 0$
11. $3x^2 - 27 = 0$
12. $4x^2 - 100 = 0$
13. $9x^2 - 1 = 0$
14. $25x^2 - 4 = 0$
15. $16x^2 - 4 = 0$

Exercise 2.2C

Solve the following quadratics equations by factorising:

1. $x^2 + 5x + 6 = 0$
2. $x^2 + 12x + 36 = 0$
3. $x^2 + x - 12 = 0$
4. $x^2 - 10x + 16 = 0$
5. $x^2 - 11x + 24 = 0$
6. $x^2 - x - 6 = 0$
7. $x^2 - 9x + 18 = 0$
8. $x^2 - 13x + 42 = 0$
9. $16 - 8x + x^2 = 0$
10. $x^2 + x - 30 = 0$
11. $16 - 6x - x^2 = 0$
12. $x^2 - 10x + 24 = 0$
13. $x^2 - x - 56 = 0$
14. $x^2 + 15x + 36 = 0$
15. $12 - 4x - x^2 = 0$

Exercise 2.2D

Solve the following quadratic equations by factorising:

1. $2x^2 + 6x = 0$
2. $x^2 - 9x = 0$
3. $3x^2 - 3 = 0$
4. $x^2 - 8x + 7 = 0$
5. $4x^2 - 8x - 12 = 0$
6. $3x^2 + 3x - 18 = 0$
7. $x^2 - 4 = 0$
8. $6x^2 + 12x = 0$
9. $3x^2 + 2x - 5 = 0$
10. $x^2 - 13x + 40 = 0$
11. $x^2 - 6x + 9 = 0$
12. $x^2 - 4x - 21 = 0$
13. $x^2 - x - 72 = 0$
14. $6 - x - x^2 = 0$
15. $24 + 5x - x^2 = 0$
16. $12x^2 + 60x = 0$
17. $x^2 + 4x - 12 = 0$
18. $5x^2 - 55x + 50 = 0$
19. $100 - 25x^2 = 0$
20. $6 + x - x^2 = 0$
21. $24x - 8x^2 = 0$
22. $x^2 + 8x + 12 = 0$
23. $8x^2 - 28x + 12 = 0$
24. $75 - 3x^2 = 0$
25. $5x^2 - 125 = 0$
26. $x^2 - 15x + 54 = 0$
27. $48 - 12x^2 = 0$
28. $4x^2 - 12x - 27 = 0$
29. $15 + 2x - x^2 = 0$
30. $60 - 26x - 6x^2 = 0$

2.3 Solving Quadratics by Rearranging

If a quadratic equation is not equal to zero, it needs to be rearranged to be solved.

Worked Examples:

Solve the following quadratic equations:

1. $x^2 - 3x = 4$

$x^2 - 3x - 4 = 0$

$(x - 4)(x + 1) = 0$

$x - 4 = 0$ or $x + 1 = 0$

$x = 4$ $x = -1$

2. $x^2 = 5x - 6$

$x^2 - 5x + 6 = 0$

$(x - 3)(x - 2) = 0$

$x - 3 = 0$ or $x - 2 = 0$

$x = 3$ $x = 2$

3. $2x^2 + 12 - 6x = x^2 + 2x$

$x^2 - 8x + 12 = 0$

$(x - 2)(x - 6) = 0$

$x - 2 = 0$ or $x - 6 = 0$

$x = 2$ $x = 6$

Exercise 2.3

Solve the following quadratics equations:

1. $2x^2 = 6x$

2. $x^2 = 16$

3. $2x^2 = 8x$

4. $x^2 = 8x - 7$

5. $x^2 = 7x - 12$

6. $x^2 = 1$

7. $2x^2 = 4x$

8. $12x = x^2$

9. $2x - 1 = x^2$

10. $x^2 + 40 = 13x$

11. $6x + 12 = 3 - x^2$

12. $x^2 - 2x - 6 = 15 + 2x$

13. $x^2 + 3x - 36 = 4x + 36$

14. $6 + 7x - 2x^2 = 2x - x^2$

15. $3x^2 + 24 + 3x = 4x^2 - 2x$

16. $15x^2 = 60x$

17. $x^2 + 3 = 15 - 4x$

18. $18 = x^2 + 3x$

19. $\dfrac{2x^2 - 12}{x} = 5$

20. $3x - 5 = \dfrac{2}{x}$

21. $\dfrac{5x^2 + 3}{16} = x$

22. $(x + 3)(x - 4) = 3x$

23. $x(x + 5) - 2(x - 1) = 12$

24. $\dfrac{x^2 + 6}{7} = x$

25. $\dfrac{x^2 + 1}{(x - 1)} = 5$

26. $(x + 5)(x - 6) = 6x$

27. $\dfrac{8x - 12}{x} = x$

28. $x(x - 4) + x(x - 9) = 15$

29. $\dfrac{(x - 1)^2}{x + 11} = 1$

30. $\dfrac{8 - 6x}{x} = 5x$

When a quadratic function is difficult to factorise (usually because the factors are not whole numbers), the function can be solved using the **Quadratic Formula**.

The formula is $x = \dfrac{-b \pm \sqrt{b^2 - 4ac}}{2a}$, where $ax^2 + bx + c$

NB: The expression $b^2 - 4ac$ is known as the **discriminant** (see sections **2.6** and **3.3** of this chapter). A quadratic function will only have real solutions when $b^2 - 4ac \geq 0$.

Worked Examples:

1. Solve the quadratic equation $x^2 + 3x - 1 = 0$ to 1 decimal place.

Since $ax^2 + bx + c$, then $a = 1, b = 3, c = -1$

$$x = \frac{-b \pm \sqrt{b^2 - 4ac}}{2a}$$

$$x = \frac{-(3) \pm \sqrt{(3)^2 - 4(1)(-1)}}{2(1)}$$

$$x = \frac{-3 - \sqrt{13}}{2} \quad \text{or} \quad x = \frac{-3 + \sqrt{13}}{2}$$

$$x = -3.3 \text{ (to 1 d.p.)} \qquad x = 0.3 \text{ (to 1 d.p.)}$$

Exercise 2.4

Solve the following quadratic equations to 1 decimal place using the quadratic formula:

1. $x^2 + 4x - 6 = 0$

2. $2x^2 + 7x - 6 = 0$

3. $x^2 + 4x - 2 = 0$

4. $x^2 - 5x + 3 = 0$

5. $x^2 - 6x + 4 = 0$

6. $x^2 - 3x - 2 = 0$

7. $x^2 + 9x - 11 = 0$

8. $2x^2 + 13x + 10 = 0$

9. $x^2 - 8x - 2 = 0$

10. $6 - 9x - x^2 = 0$

11. $x^2 + 8x - 15 = 0$

12. $3 - 10x - 3x^2 = 0$

13. $2x^2 + 9x + 1 = 0$

14. $x^2 - 3 = 0$

15. $x^2 - 4x - 1 = 0$

16. $5 - 9x - x^2 = 0$

17. $1 - 5x - x^2 = 0$

18. $6 - 10x - x^2 = 0$

19. $x^2 = 7x + 1$

20. $x^2 = 3x - 1$

21. $x^2 = 4x - 1$

22. $2 = 9x - 2x^2$

23. $2x^2 + 8x = 2$

24. $2 - 10x = 3x^2$

25. $3x^2 = 8x + 2$

26. $3x^2 - 3 = 13x$

27. $5x^2 = 5x - 1$

28. $1 = 3x^2 - 11x$

29. $2x^2 - 6x = 3$

30. $2x^2 = 8x - 1$

2.5 Forming Quadratic Equations

Quadratic equations can be used to solve problems.

Worked Examples:

1. The rectangle and the square have the same area. By forming an equation, find the dimensions of the rectangle.

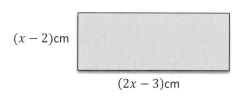

$(x-2)$cm

$(2x-3)$cm

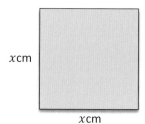

$x$cm

$x$cm

$$(2x-3)(x-2) = x^2$$
$$2x^2 - 7x + 6 = x^2$$
$$x^2 - 7x + 6 = 0$$
$$(x-6)(x-1) = 0$$
$$x - 6 = 0 \quad or \quad x - 1 = 0$$
$$x = 6 \quad or \quad \cancel{x = 1}$$

∴ Length = $2(6) - 3 = 9$cm

Breadth = $6 - 2 = 4$cm

NB: When $x = 1$ the length and breadth of the rectangle would be negative ∴ $x = 1$ is not a solution.

2. The dimensions of the rectangle below are increased by x in both length and breadth. The area of the new rectangle is 288cm². Find the new length and breadth of the rectangle.

10cm

12cm

$$(x+10)(x+12) = 288$$
$$x^2 + 22x + 120 = 288$$
$$x^2 + 22x - 168 = 0$$
$$(x-6)(x+28) = 0$$
$$x - 6 = 0 \quad or \quad x + 28 = 0$$
$$x = 6 \quad or \quad \cancel{x = -28}$$

∴ Length = $6 + 12 = 18$cm

Breadth = $6 + 10 = 16$cm

Exercise 2.5

<u>By forming and solving an equation</u>, find the dimensions of the following rectangles:

1. Area = 12 cm²

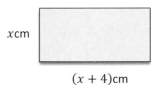

$x$cm

$(x + 4)$cm

2. Area = 28 cm²

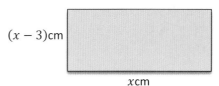

$(x - 3)$cm

$x$cm

3. Area = 14 cm²

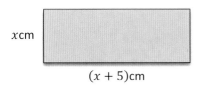

$x$cm

$(x + 5)$cm

4. Area = 24 cm²

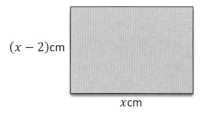

$(x - 2)$cm

$x$cm

5. Area = 60 cm²

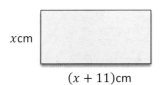

$x$cm

$(x + 11)$cm

6. Area = 36 cm²

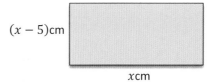

$(x - 5)$cm

$x$cm

7. Area = 20 cm²

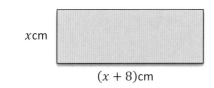

$x$cm

$(x + 8)$cm

8. Area = 78 cm²

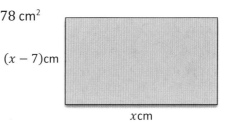

$(x - 7)$cm

$x$cm

9. Area = 63 cm²

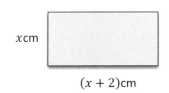

$x$cm

$(x + 2)$cm

10. Area = 18 cm²

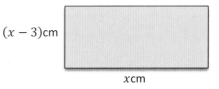

$(x - 3)$cm

$x$cm

11. Area = 100 cm²

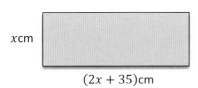

$x$cm

$(2x + 35)$cm

12. Area = 45 cm²

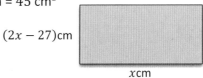

$(2x - 27)$cm

$x$cm

13. The two shapes below have the same area. By forming an equation, find the area of each shape.

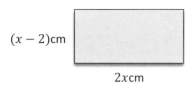

$(x - 2)$cm

$2x$cm

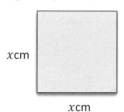

$x$cm

$x$cm

14. The two shapes below have the same area. By forming an equation, find the area of each shape.

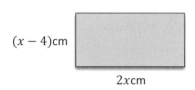

$(x - 4)$cm

$2x$cm

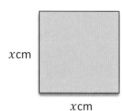

$x$cm

$x$cm

15. The two shapes below have the same area. By forming an equation, find the area of each shape.

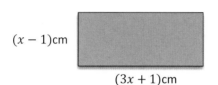

$(x - 1)$cm

$(3x + 1)$cm

$(x - 3)$cm

$(5x + 7)$cm

16. The two shapes below have the same area. By forming an equation, find the area of each shape.

$(x - 1)$cm

$(x + 4)$cm

$(2x - 7)$cm

$(x + 7)$cm

17. The two shapes below have the same area. By forming an equation, find the area of each shape.

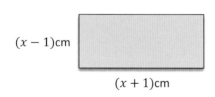

$(x - 1)$cm

$(x + 1)$cm

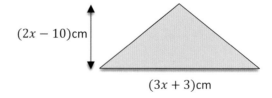

$(2x - 10)$cm

$(3x + 3)$cm

18. The two shapes below have the same area. By forming an equation, find the area of each shape.

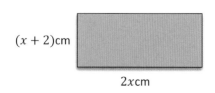

$(x + 2)$cm

$2x$cm

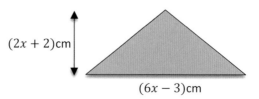

$(2x + 2)$cm

$(6x - 3)$cm

19. The two shapes below have the same area. By forming an equation, find the area of each shape.

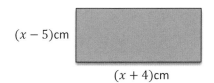

$(x-5)$cm

$(x+4)$cm

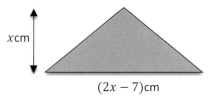

$x$cm

$(2x-7)$cm

20. The dimensions of the rectangle below are increased by x in both length and breadth. The area of the new rectangle is 176cm^2. Find the new length and breadth of the rectangle.

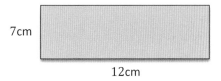

7cm

12cm

21. The dimensions of the rectangle below are increased by x in both length and breadth. The area of the new rectangle is 140cm^2. Find the new length and breadth of the rectangle.

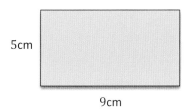

5cm

9cm

22. A rectangular lawn is 10 metres wide and 12 metres long and has a border around two sides, x metres wide. The area of the garden with the border is 143 m^2, find the width of the border.

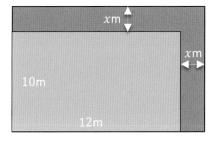

xm

xm

10m

12m

23. The area of a mirror including the frame is 600cm^2. By forming an equation, find the width of the frame.

$x$cm

10cm

20cm

$x$cm

The formula $b^2 - 4ac$, where $ax^2 + bx + c$ is known as the **discriminant**. The discriminant is used to determine the *nature of the roots*, or the points of intersection between a quadratic curve and the x-axis.

There are three results that matter when calculating the discriminant:

$b^2 - 4ac > 0$ this means there are **two real and distinct roots, i.e.** the curve cuts the x-axis in two different places.

$b^2 - 4ac = 0$ this means there are **two real and equal roots, i.e.** the x-axis is a tangent to the curve.

$b^2 - 4ac < 0$ this means there are **no real roots, i.e.** the curve does not cut the x-axis.

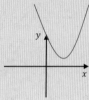

Worked Examples:

1. State the nature of the roots of the quadratic equation $x^2 + 3x - 1 = 0$.

    Since $ax^2 + bx + c$, then $a = 1, b = 3, c = -1$

    $b^2 - 4ac = (3)^2 - 4(1)(-1) = 9 + 4 = 13$

    $b^2 - 4ac > 0$, ∴ there are two real and distinct roots.

2. State the nature of the roots of the quadratic equation $2x^2 - 3x + 6 = 0$.

    Since $ax^2 + bx + c$, then $a = 2, b = -3, c = 6$

    $b^2 - 4ac = (-3)^2 - 4(2)(6) = 9 - 48 = -39$

    $b^2 - 4ac < 0$, ∴ there are no real roots.

3. State the nature of the roots of the quadratic equation $x^2 = 8x - 16$.

    Since $ax^2 + bx + c$, the quadratic needs to be rearranged:

    $x^2 = 8x - 16$

    $x^2 - 8x + 16 = 0$

    then $a = 1, b = -8, c = 16$

    $b^2 - 4ac = (-8)^2 - 4(1)(16) = 64 - 64 = 0$

    $b^2 - 4ac = 0$, ∴ there are two real and equal roots.

Exercise 2.6

Determine the nature of the roots of the following quadratic equations:

1. $x^2 + 4x - 6 = 0$
2. $2x^2 + 7x + 8 = 0$
3. $x^2 + 4x + 2 = 0$

4. $x^2 - 5x + 6 = 0$
5. $x^2 - 6x + 7 = 0$
6. $x^2 - 3x + 3 = 0$

7. $x^2 + 10x - 10 = 0$
8. $x^2 + 10x + 25 = 0$
9. $x^2 - 9 = 0$

10. $10 - 7x - x^2 = 0$
11. $x^2 + 8x + 25 = 0$
12. $3 - 8 - 3x^2 = 0$

13. $2x^2 + 1 = 0$
14. $4x^2 - 3 = 0$
15. $x^2 - 4x = 0$

16. $5 - x^2 = 0$
17. $1 - 5x - x^2 = 0$
18. $12 + x^2 = 0$

19. $x^2 = 6x - 9$
20. $x^2 = -2$
21. $x^2 = 2x - 1$

22. $5 = 9x - 4x^2$
23. $2x^2 = 2x$
24. $7 - 5x = 3x^2$

25. $3x^2 = 6x - 2$
26. $3x^2 + 3 = 6x$
27. $5x^2 = 5x - 1$

28. $16 = x^2 + 8x$
29. $x^2 = 36 - 12x$
30. $2x^2 = -1$

2.7 Using the Discriminant

When the roots of a quadratic equation are not known, but the nature of the roots are, the discriminant can be used to find the unknown coefficients.

Worked Examples:

1. State the values of k for which the equation $x^2 + kx + 1 = 0$ has equal roots.

   Since $ax^2 + bx + c$, then $a = 1, b = k, c = 1$ and the quadratic has equal roots so,

   $b^2 - 4ac = 0$

   $k^2 - 4(1)(1) = 0$

   $k^2 - 4 = 0$

   $k^2 = 4$

   $k = \pm 2$

2. State the values of k for which the equation $x^2 + (4 - k)x + 1 = 0$ has equal roots.

   Since $ax^2 + bx + c$, then $a = 1, b = (4 - k), c = 1$ and the quadratic has equal roots so,

   $b^2 - 4ac = 0$

   $(4 - k)^2 - 4(1)(1) = 0$

   $16 - 8k + k^2 - 4 = 0$

   $12 - 8k + k^2 = 0$

   $(6 - k)(2 - k) = 0$

   $6 - k = 0$ or $2 - k = 0$

   $k = 6$ or $k = 2$

Exercise 2.7

Find the value(s) of k for which these quadratic equations have equal roots:

1. $x^2 + 6x + k = 0$
2. $x^2 - kx + 4 = 0$
3. $x^2 + kx + 9 = 0$

4. $kx^2 + 8x + 2 = 0$
5. $kx^2 + 6x + k = 0$
6. $kx^2 - 8x + k = 0$

7. $x^2 + 2kx + 2k = 0$
8. $x^2 + 2kx + 5k = 0$
9. $x^2 + (2 - k)x + k + 6 = 0$

10. $x^2 + (k + 1)x + k + 9 = 0$
11. $x^2 + (5 - k)x + k + 3 = 0$
12. $x^2 + kx + 7x + k + 10 = 0$

13. $x^2 + kx + 3x + k = -11$
14. $x^2 + 2x + k = kx + 2$
15. $x^2 + kx + 4k = 11x - 21$

3.1 Solving Quadratics by Completing the Square

When the roots of a quadratic equation are not rational numbers (**i.e.** they cannot be expressed as an integer or a fraction), it can be solved by method of completing the square. This is a non-calculator alternative to the **Quadratic Formula** (see **chapter 9** for more explanation). It is important to first determine whether the quadratic function can be solved by using the **discriminant** (see above).

Worked Examples:

1.
$$x^2 + 4x + 3 = 0$$
$$(x^2 + 4x) + 3 = 0$$
$$(x + 2)^2 + 3 - 4 = 0$$
$$(x + 2)^2 - 1 = 0$$
$$(x + 2)^2 = 1$$
$$x + 2 = \pm 1$$
$$x = 1 - 2 \quad or \quad x = -1$$
$$x = -1 \qquad\qquad x = -3$$

2.
$$x^2 - 6x + 12 = 0$$
$$(x^2 - 6x) + 12 = 0$$
$$(x - 3)^2 + 12 - 9 = 0$$
$$(x - 3)^2 + 3 = 0$$
$$(x - 3)^2 = 3$$
$$x - 3 = \pm\sqrt{3}$$
$$x = 3 + \sqrt{3} \quad or \quad x = 3 - \sqrt{3}$$

NB: Example 1 may be solved by factorising as the solutions are integers.

Exercise 3.1

Solve the following quadratic equations by completing the square:

1. $x^2 + 4x - 5 = 0$
2. $x^2 + 6x + 5 = 0$
3. $x^2 + 10x + 9 = 0$

4. $x^2 - 8x + 7 = 0$
5. $x^2 - 6x - 7 = 0$
6. $x^2 - 2x - 24 = 0$

7. $x^2 + 2x - 2 = 0$
8. $x^2 + 4x + 1 = 0$
9. $x^2 + 6x - 2 = 0$

10. $x^2 - 4x - 3 = 0$
11. $x^2 + 8x + 10 = 0$
12. $x^2 - 4x - 8 = 0$

13. $x^2 + 10x + 20 = 0$
14. $x^2 - 6x - 3 = 0$
15. $x^2 - 4x - 20 = 0$

16. $x^2 + 2x - 1 = 0$

17. $x^2 - 12x + 18 = 0$

18. $x^2 + 8x + 4 = 0$

19. $x^2 - 8x - 8 = 0$

20. $2x^2 - 4x + 1 = 0$

21. $2x^2 + 6x - 1 = 0$

22. $4x^2 - 16x + 3 = 0$

23. $2x^2 + 12x - 3 = 0$

24. $3x^2 + 18x + 3 = 0$

25. $3x^2 - 12x - 2 = 0$

26. $3x^2 + 6x - 4 = 0$

27. $5x^2 + 20x - 1 = 0$

28. $6x^2 - 24x + 1 = 0$

29. $8x^2 + 32x + 3 = 0$

30. $3x^2 + 36x - 1 = 0$

3.2 Solving Quadratic Inequations

To solve a quadratic inequation: find the roots, draw a sketch and answer the question. There are two types of solution to a quadratic inequation, a **bounded solution**, which is between the two roots of the quadratic (example 1) and an **unbounded solution**, which involves two separate values of x (example 2). To find where a quadratic function is less than zero is to find where the graph is below the x-axis and to find where it is greater than zero is to find where the graph is above the x-axis.

Worked Examples:

Solve the following quadratic inequations:

1. $x^2 - 4x + 3 < 0$

     $(x - 1)(x - 3) = 0$

   $x - 1 = 0$ or $x - 3 = 0$

      $x = 1$ $x = 3$

     $\therefore x^2 - 4x + 3 < 0$ for $1 < x < 3$

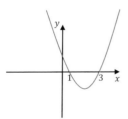

This quadratic is positive as the coefficient of x^2 is greater than zero, therefore the graph has a **minimum turning point**. The roots are $x = 1$ and $x = 3$. To solve the inequation $x^2 - 4x + 3 < 0$ is to find where the graph is below the x-axis.

2. $6 - x - x^2 \leq 0$

     $(3 + x)(2 - x) = 0$

   $3 + x = 0$ or $2 - x = 0$

      $x = -3$ $x = 2$

     $\therefore 6 - x - x^2 \leq 0$ for $x \leq -3$ and $x \geq 2$

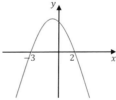

This quadratic is negative as the coefficient of x^2 is less than zero, therefore the graph has a **maximum turning point**.

Exercise 3.2

Solve the following quadratic inequations:

1. $2x^2 + 6x < 0$

2. $x^2 - 8x > 0$

3. $x^2 - 4 \leq 0$

4. $x^2 - 8x + 7 \geq 0$

5. $x^2 - 2x - 3 < 0$

6. $3x^2 + 3x - 18 > 0$

7. $x^2 - 9 < 0$

8. $5x^2 + 10x \geq 0$

9. $x^2 + 2x - 8 > 0$

10. $x^2 - x - 6 \leq 0$

11. $x^2 - 4x - 12 < 0$

12. $x^2 - 4x - 21 < 0$

13. $x^2 - 5x - 36 > 0$

14. $4 - 3x - x^2 < 0$

15. $6 + 5x - x^2 \geq 0$

16. $10x^2 + 60x \leq 0$

17. $x^2 + 11x - 12 > 0$

18. $x^2 - 11x + 10 \leq 0$

19. $100 - 25x^2 < 0$

20. $6 - x - x^2 \leq 0$

21. $16x - 8x^2 > 0$

22. $x^2 + 5x + 6 \leq 0$

23. $x^2 - 7x + 6 > 0$

24. $75 - 3x^2 \geq 0$

25. $x^2 - 3 > 0$

26. $x^2 - 15x + 36 < 0$

27. $2 - x^2 > 0$

28. $x^2 - 3x - 18 < 0$

29. $15 + 2x - x^2 > 0$

30. $12 - 11x - x^2 \leq 0$

3.3 Solving Quadratics – Mixed Exercise (Non-Calculator)

Exercise 3.3

For each of the following quadratics, solve where possible by the most suitable means:

1. $x^2 + x - 6 = 0$

2. $2x^2 + 3x + 8 = 0$

3. $x^2 + x - 2 = 0$

4. $x^2 - 6x + 6 = 0$

5. $x^2 + 6x - 7 = 0$

6. $x^2 - 2x - 3 = 0$

7. $x^2 + 10x - 25 = 0$

8. $2x^2 - 50 = 0$

9. $3x^2 - 9x - 12 = 0$

10. $10 - 6x - x^2 = 0$

11. $x^2 + 8x + 15 = 0$

12. $x^2 - 8x + 15 \geq 0$

13. $2x^2 = 1$

14. $4x^2 - 3 = 0$

15. $x^2 - 4x - 1 = 0$

16. $5 - x^2 \leq 0$

17. $1 - 4x - x^2 = 0$

18. $12 + 7x + x^2 = 0$

19. $x^2 - 6x = 7$

20. $x^2 + 1 = -2$

21. $x^2 - 2x = -5$

22. $1 - 8x - 4x^2 = 0$

23. $2x^2 = 2x$

24. $7 - 6x = 3x^2$

25. $3x^2 = 6x - 2$

26. $3x^2 + 3 < 6x$

27. $5x^2 = 5x - 1$

28. $16 = x^2 - 8x$

29. $x^2 = 36 - 12x$

30. $3x^2 - 1 > 0$

Chapter 11
Solving Equations 4 – Further Solving Equations

3.1 Solving Polynomials

Polynomials include quadratic functions but are not limited to them (see **chapter 3, section 3.1, page 29**). To solve polynomials, they need to be factorised using **synthetic division** and then solved in the same way as quadratic functions.

Worked Example:

Solve the polynomial $x^3 - 3x + 2 = 0$.

$$x^3 - 3x + 2 = 0$$
$$(x + 2)(x^2 - 2x + 1) = 0$$
$$(x + 2)(x - 1)(x - 1) = 0$$
$$(x + 2) = 0 \quad \text{or} \quad (x - 1) = 0 \text{ twice}$$
$$x = -2 \quad \text{or} \quad x = 1 \text{ twice}$$

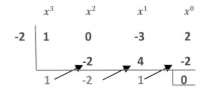

Exercise 3.1

Solve each of the following polynomial equations:

1. $x^3 + 3x^2 - x - 3 = 0$

2. $x^3 + 3x^2 - 6x - 8 = 0$

3. $x^3 - x^2 - 8x + 12 = 0$

4. $x^3 - 4x^2 + x + 6 = 0$

5. $x^4 - 6x^2 - 27 = 0$

6. $x^3 - 3x - 2 = 0$

7. $x^3 - 5x^2 + 8x - 4 = 0$

8. $x^3 + 5x^2 + 2x - 8 = 0$

9. $x^4 - 16 = 0$

10. $x^3 - 28x + 48 = 0$

11. $x^3 - 6x^2 + 12x - 8 = 0$

12. $2x^3 + 3x^2 - 8x + 3 = 0$

13. $x^3 + 7x^2 - 36 = 0$

14. $x^3 - x^2 - 22x + 40 = 0$

15. $x^3 - 2x^2 - 4x + 8 = 0$

16. $x^4 - 15x^2 - 16 = 0$

17. $x^4 + 2x^2 - 3 = 0$

18. $x^3 + 4x^2 + x - 6 = 0$

19. $x^3 + x^2 - 25x - 25 = 0$

20. $x^4 - 5x^3 + 9x^2 - 7x + 2 = 0$

21. $x^3 - 3x^2 - 24x + 80 = 0$

22. $4x^3 + 4x^2 - x - 1 = 0$

23. $x^3 + 4x^2 - 9x - 36 = 0$

24. $x^4 - 2x^2 + 1 = 0$

25. $x^3 + 4x^2 - 7x - 10 = 0$

26. $x^3 + 5x^2 + 3x - 9 = 0$

27. $x^4 - 6x^3 + 8x^2 + 6x - 9 = 0$

3.2 Simultaneous Equations with a Line and a Curve

The point of intersection between a line and a curve can be found by solving the two equations simultaneously by method of **substitution** (see **chapter 6 section 2.1, page 54**).

Worked Example:

Find the points of intersection between the line $y = 2x - 4$ and the curve $y = x^3 - x^2 - 4$.

As both line and curve are equal to y, they can be equated:

$$x^3 - x^2 - 4 = 2x - 4$$
$$x^3 - x^2 - 2x = 0$$
$$x(x^2 - x - 2) = 0$$
$$x(x - 2)(x + 1) = 0$$
$$x = 0, \quad (x - 2) = 0 \quad \text{or} \quad (x + 1) = 0$$
$$x = 0, \quad x = 2 \quad \text{or} \quad x = -1$$

Substitute x-values into line to find y-coordinate.

When $x = 0, y = 2(0) - 4 = -4$

When $x = 2, y = 2(2) - 4 = 0$

When $x = -1, y = 2(-1) - 4 = -6$

Points of intersection are $(0, -4)$, $(2, 0)$ and $(-1, -6)$.

> **NB:** Synthetic division may be needed to solve the equation (see **section 3.1**).

Exercise 3.2

Find the point(s) of intersection between the line and the curve:

1. $y = x^2 - 3x + 4$
   $y = x + 1$

2. $y = x^2 - 5x + 4$
   $y = x - 4$

3. $y = x^2 - 5x + 8$
   $y = x + 3$

4. $y = x^2 - 5x - 21$
   $y = x - 5$

5. $y = x^2 - 5x + 1$
   $x - y = 8$

6. $y = x^2 + 2x - 25$
   $x - y = 5$

7. $y = 2x^2 - 3x - 4$
   $x - y = 6$

8. $y = 2x^2 + x - 13$
   $x + y + 1 = 0$

9. $y = x^3 + x^2 - 5x - 1$
   $x + y = 3$

10. $y = x^3 - 2x^2 + 5x - 1$
    $2x + y = 5$

11. $y = x^3 + x^2 - 5x - 5$
    $x - y = 5$

12. $y = x^3 - 5x - 1$
    $x + y = -1$

13. $y = x^3 + x^2$
    $x - y = -1$

14. $y = x^3 + x^2 - 3x - 6$
    $x - y = 2$

15. $y = x^3 - 3x^2 + x + 7$
    $x - y = -3$

3.3 Simultaneous Equations with a Line and a Circle

The points of intersection between a line and a circle can be found by solving the equations simultaneously by method of **substitution** (see **chapter 6 section 2.1, page 54**).

Worked Example:

Find the points of intersection between the line $y = 2x + 5$ and the circle

$x^2 + y^2 + 4x - 2y = 0.$

The line can be substituted into the circle to form a quadratic equation:

$$x^2 + y^2 + 4x - 2y = 0$$
$$x^2 + (2x + 5)^2 + 4x - 2(2x + 5) = 0$$
$$x^2 + 4x^2 + 20x + 25 + 4x - 4x - 10 = 0$$
$$5x^2 + 20x + 15 = 0$$
$$5(x^2 + 4x + 3) = 0$$
$$5(x + 3)(x + 1) = 0$$
$$(x + 3) = 0 \quad \text{or} \quad (x + 1) = 0$$
$$x = -3 \quad \text{or} \quad x = -1$$

Substitute x-values into line to find y-coordinate.

When $x = -3, y = 2(-3) + 5 = -1$

When $x = -1, y = 2(-1) + 5 = 3$

Points of intersection are $(-3, -1)$ and $(-1, 3)$.

Exercise 3.3

Find the point(s) of intersection between the line and the circle:

1. $x^2 + y^2 - 2x + 4y + 5 = 0$
   $y = -2x$

2. $x^2 + y^2 = 13$
   $y = x + 1$

3. $x^2 + y^2 = 25$
   $y = 3x - 5$

4. $x^2 + y^2 - 2x - 3 = 0$
   $y = x - 3$

5. $x^2 + y^2 = 29$
   $y = x - 7$

6. $x^2 + y^2 - 2x + 4y - 20 = 0$
   $y = 2x + 1$

7. $x^2 + y^2 - 6y - 20 = 0$
   $y = x - 4$

8. $x^2 + y^2 + 4x - 8y - 41 = 0$
   $x + y - 1 = 0$

9. $(x - 2)^2 + (y + 1)^2 = 20$
   $y = 2x + 5$

10. $(x - 1)^2 + (y - 2)^2 = 4$
    $y = x - 1$

11. $(x - 3)^2 + (y - 2)^2 = 17$
    $y = x - 4$

12. $x^2 + y^2 + 6y - 1 = 0$
    $x - y - 7 = 0$

13. $x^2 + y^2 - 4x + 6y - 45 = 0$
    $y = x + 5$

14. $x^2 + y^2 = 25$
    $y = -x - 7$

15. $x^2 + y^2 - 8x - 24 = 0$
    $y = x - 8$

Answers

Chapter 1

1. $2a$ 2. $3b$ 3. $5c$ 4. $4d$
5. $4e$ 6. $6f$ 7. $5g$ 8. $2h$
9. $6i$ 10. $3j$ 11. $7k$ 12. $8l$
13. $3a+2b$ 14. $3c+2d$ 15. $3e+4f$ 16. $3g+3h$
17. $3j+2k$ 18. $4m+3n$ 19. $3a+2b$ 20. $3c+3d$
21. $5e+3f$ 22. $2g+3h$ 23. $2j+3k$ 24. $2a+2b+2c$
25. $2a$ 26. b 27. $3c$ 28. 0
29. e 30. $3f$ 31. $3a$ 32. $3c-3d$
33. $e+f$ 34. $3h$ 35. $-2j-k$ 36. 0

1. $4a$ 2. $6b$ 3. $7c$
4. $12d$ 5. $9e$ 6. $12f$
7. $8a+3b$ 8. $14c+6d$ 9. $17e+23f$
10. $12g+11h$ 11. $23j+105k$ 12. $14m+7n+13p$
13. $3a$ 14. $2b$ 15. $3c$
16. $5d$ 17. $15e$ 18. $-2f$
19. $2a+2b$ 20. $6c-3d$ 21. $-e+6f$
22. $3g-h$ 23. $-j+k$ 24. $7a-8b-3c$
25. $x+10y-5$ 26. $2c-4d+7$ 27. $2r+2s-2$
28. $11p-3q-3$ 29. $4m-10n+7$ 30. $-4x-5y-3$

1. $5a$ 2. $6b$ 3. $7c$ 4. $8d$
5. $9e$ 6. $13f$ 7. $8g$ 8. $21h$
9. $36i$ 10. $20j$ 11. $12k$ 12. $14l$
13. $24m$ 14. $15n$ 15. $18p$ 16. $12q$
17. $64r$ 18. $14s$ 19. $36t$ 20. $26u$
21. $42v$ 22. $6x$ 23. $24y$ 24. $60z$

1. ab 2. bc 3. ac 4. bd
5. efg 6. gd 7. km 8. trs
9. n^2 10. m^2 11. gb^2 12. w^2r

1. $3ab$ 2. $5cg$ 3. $10ch$ 4. $18ad$
5. $6efg$ 6. $40de$ 7. $2hm$ 8. $27en$
9. $12abc$ 10. $8stu$ 11. $9cdsv$ 12. $12t^2$
13. $12m^2$ 14. $15b^2$ 15. $18a^2b$ 16. $12bc^2d$
17. $40r^2$ 18. $14bsv^2$ 19. $6a^2b^2$ 20. $8w^2z^2$
21. $12pr^2$ 22. $6x^2v$ 23. $32b^2c$ 24. $50d^2g^2$

1. $3a$ 2. $4b$ 3. $6c$ 4. $7d$
5. $-3e$ 6. f 7. $-3g$ 8. $3h$
9. $2i$ 10. $10j$ 11. $6k$ 12. $9m$
13. 0 14. $7p$ 15. $7q$ 16. $11r$
17. $8r^2$ 18. $-2s^2$ 19. $3wx$ 20. $-wy$
21. $-13z$ 22. $14a$ 23. $-2b$ 24. $-c$
25. $-4d$ 26. $13e$ 27. $11f$ 28. $4g$

1. $\dfrac{1}{6}$ 2. 5 3. 2 4. $\dfrac{1}{4}$
5. $\dfrac{1}{2e}$ 6. $\dfrac{1}{5}$ 7. $\dfrac{1}{6}$ 8. 8
9. $\dfrac{2}{r}$ 10. h 11. $\dfrac{2}{j}$ 12. $\dfrac{3m}{4}$
13. 8 14. $\dfrac{r}{2}$ 15. $\dfrac{3}{4n}$ 16. $\dfrac{1}{3}$
17. 2 18. $\dfrac{1}{2}$ 19. $\dfrac{1}{3}$ 20. $\dfrac{1}{2}$
21. 2 22. $\dfrac{4}{5}$ 23. $\dfrac{1}{3}$ 24. 2
25. h 26. $\dfrac{1}{k}$ 27. p 28. r
29. $\dfrac{1}{v}$ 30. $\dfrac{1}{xy}$ 31. $2a$ 32. $\dfrac{1}{2c}$
33. $\dfrac{3}{2d}$ 34. $\dfrac{2}{f}$ 35. $\dfrac{1}{3h}$ 36. $\dfrac{x}{5}$
37. $\dfrac{3b}{2}$ 38. y 39. $\dfrac{1}{a}$ 40. $\dfrac{bc}{5}$
41. $\dfrac{2f}{d}$ 42. $\dfrac{2b^2}{c}$ 43. $\dfrac{3x}{2}$ 44. $\dfrac{3su}{2t}$
45. $\dfrac{8}{9mp}$

1. $5a$ 2. $10b^2$ 3. $9c$ 4. $5a+2b$
5. $6dg$ 6. $3e$ 7. $2r^2m$ 8. $3d$
9. $4trs$ 10. $2s+3t$ 11. $2y$ 12. $12g^2$
13. $4mn^2p$ 14. $-2a$ 15. $2z$ 16. $a+2$
17. $6x+5$ 18. $4b$ 19. $\dfrac{1}{2c}$ 20. $8w^2z^2$
21. $12pr^2$ 22. $6vx^2$ 23. $32b^2c$ 24. $7g^2$
25. $3b+2$ 26. $-b^2$ 27. 0 28. $3d$
29. $6x^2y$ 30. $12y^2z^2$ 31. $3b$ 32. $6e+4f$
33. 1 34. $6s$ 35. $18v$ 36. $3s$
37. $-7h$ 38. $7t$ 39. $17e$ 40. $-3w^2$
41. $-10sr$ 42. $-8v^2w$ 43. $2k$ 44. $6z^2$
45. $20r^2s$ 46. $6y$ 47. $5a^2$ 48. $-3e^2$

1. a^2 2. b^2 3. c^3 4. d^5
5. e^6 6. f^5 7. g^9 8. h^8
9. j^{13} 10. k^{23} 11. m^7 12. n^{10}
13. p^{25} 14. q^6 15. r^4 16. s^4
17. t^4 18. $6u^{10}$ 19. $20v^{22}$ 20. $24w^{21}$
21. $72x^{12}$ 22. $33y^{16}$ 23. $30z^9$ 24. $144e^6$
25. $30a^{-10}$ 26. $36b^{18}$ 27. $55c^{43}$ 28. $72d^0$ (or 72)
29. $120e^{-3}$ 30. $36s^{-1}$ 31. $10x$ 32. $44z^0$ (or 44)

1. a^2 2. b 3. c^2 4. d
5. e^3 6. f^5 7. g^4 8. h^4
9. j^{19} 10. k^{11} 11. m^5 12. n^4
13. p^7 14. 1 15. r^{11} 16. $2s^3$
17. $11t^2$ 18. $\dfrac{u^2}{2}$ 19. $\dfrac{v^7}{3}$ 20. $\dfrac{3w^9}{4}$
21. xy^2 22. w^2x 23. c^7d^3 24. e^3
25. $m^7n^3p^3$ 26. $3de^4$ 27. $\dfrac{2b^2c^3}{3}$ 28. $\dfrac{xz}{9}$

29. $\frac{3s^6tu^8}{4}$ **30.** $\frac{2}{3}$

1. a^4 **2.** b^2 **3.** c^6 **4.** 1

5. e **6.** $\frac{3f^4}{2}$ **7.** $6g^6$ **8.** $9h^3$

9. $\frac{j}{2}$ **10.** $\frac{k^3}{2}$ **11.** $\frac{1}{3}$ **12.** $\frac{2}{3n^3}$

13. $\frac{2}{3}$ **14.** $\frac{5}{8q^2}$ **15.** $\frac{1}{8r^4}$ **16.** $\frac{s^3}{2}$

17. $\frac{3}{2t^6}$ **18.** $\frac{1}{3u^3}$ **19.** 4 **20.** $\frac{1}{2w^{-5}}$

1. a^4 **2.** b^6 **3.** c^9 **4.** d^{12}

5. e^{15} **6.** f^{20} **7.** g^{21} **8.** h^{16}

9. i^{42} **10.** j^{-10} **11.** k^{24} **12.** l^{55}

13. m^{-12} **14.** n^{-18} **15.** p^{45} **16.** x^2y^4

17. x^4y^2 **18.** x^6y^4 **19.** $x^{12}y^3z^6$ **20.** $x^{20}y^{16}z^8$

21. $4z^2$ **22.** $9x^2$ **23.** $16r^2$ **24.** $27s^3$

25. $64t^3$ **26.** $125a^3$ **27.** $16u^4$ **28.** $81v^4$

29. $25y^2$ **30.** $216p^3$ **31.** $4y^4$ **32.** $9x^6$

33. $16g^8$ **34.** $27e^{15}$ **35.** $125k^{18}$ **36.** $8a^9b^3$

37. $16r^8u^4$ **38.** $81w^{20}v^{12}$ **39.** $25x^2y^{12}$ **40.** $216n^9p^3$

1. $\frac{1}{x}$ **2.** $\frac{1}{y^2}$ **3.** $\frac{1}{z^3}$ **4.** $\frac{1}{g^5}$

5. $\frac{1}{r^4}$ **6.** $\frac{1}{h}$ **7.** $\frac{1}{w^7}$ **8.** $\frac{1}{q^8}$

9. $\frac{1}{p^2}$ **10.** $\frac{1}{u^{10}}$ **11.** $\frac{2}{r}$ **12.** $\frac{3}{p^2}$

13. $\frac{5}{e^5}$ **14.** $\frac{6}{t^3}$ **15.** $\frac{18}{n^6}$ **16.** $\frac{1}{4b^2}$

17. $\frac{1}{2d^6}$ **18.** $\frac{1}{7r^5}$ **19.** $\frac{1}{3y^4}$ **20.** $\frac{1}{8d^{10}}$

21. $\frac{5}{2b^3}$ **22.** $\frac{2}{3w^5}$ **23.** $\frac{5}{12h^6}$ **24.** $\frac{1}{3b^9}$

25. $\frac{4}{m^7}$ **26.** $\frac{1}{27a^3}$ **27.** $\frac{1}{16u^4}$ **28.** $\frac{1}{9v^2}$

29. $\frac{1}{25y^2}$ **30.** $\frac{1}{216p^3}$ **31.** $\frac{1}{4y^4}$ **32.** $\frac{1}{9e^4}$

33. $\frac{1}{16t^6}$ **34.** $\frac{1}{27m^{15}}$ **35.** $\frac{1}{125r^{18}}$ **36.** $\frac{b^3}{5}$

37. $\frac{2e^5}{11}$ **38.** $\frac{8b^3}{25}$ **39.** $\frac{2t^6}{3}$ **40.** $\frac{7r^3}{3}$

41. a^{-3} **42.** b^{-2} **43.** c^{-5} **44.** d^{-4}

45. e^{-7} **46.** $2f^{-4}$ **47.** $3g^{-7}$ **48.** $9h^{-6}$

49. $14j^{-1}$ **50.** $12k^{-8}$ **51.** $5a^{-4}$ **52.** $3b^{-5}$

53. $2c^{-2}$ **54.** $\frac{2d^{-2}}{3}$ **55.** $3e^{-4}$ **56.** $2f^{-8}$

57. $\frac{g^{-2}}{3}$ **58.** $3h^{-3}$ **59.** $\frac{3j^{-5}}{4}$ **60.** $2k^{-1}$

1. $\sqrt{x}$ **2.** $\sqrt[3]{y}$ **3.** $\sqrt[4]{p}$ **4.** $\sqrt[5]{r}$

5. $\sqrt[7]{s}$ **6.** $\sqrt{a^3}$ **7.** $\sqrt[3]{b^2}$ **8.** $\sqrt[3]{c^4}$

9. $\sqrt[6]{d}$ **10.** $\sqrt[3]{e^5}$ **11.** $\sqrt[5]{m^2}$ **12.** $\sqrt[3]{n^7}$

13. $\sqrt[6]{p^7}$ **14.** $\sqrt[9]{q^4}$ **15.** $\sqrt[3]{r^8}$ **16.** $\sqrt[7]{s^6}$

17. $\frac{1}{\sqrt{t}}$ **18.** $\frac{1}{\sqrt[3]{u^2}}$ **19.** $\frac{1}{\sqrt[5]{v^4}}$ **20.** $\frac{1}{\sqrt[7]{w^6}}$

21. $a^{\frac{1}{2}}$ **22.** $b^{\frac{1}{2}}$ **23.** $c^{\frac{3}{2}}$ **24.** $d^{\frac{5}{2}}$

25. e^2 **26.** $f^{\frac{2}{3}}$ **27.** $g^{\frac{4}{3}}$ **28.** $h^{\frac{7}{4}}$

29. $j^{\frac{3}{5}}$ **30.** $k^{\frac{5}{3}}$ **31.** $m^{\frac{5}{4}}$ **32.** $n^{\frac{3}{2}}$

33. p^2 **34.** q^4 **35.** r^3 **36.** $a^{-\frac{1}{2}}$

37. $b^{-\frac{1}{3}}$ **38.** $c^{-\frac{1}{4}}$ **39.** $d^{-\frac{1}{5}}$ **40.** $2e^{-\frac{1}{3}}$

41. $x^{-\frac{2}{3}}$ **42.** $y^{-\frac{3}{4}}$ **43.** $z^{-\frac{3}{2}}$ **44.** $g^{-\frac{3}{5}}$

45. $h^{-\frac{2}{3}}$ **46.** $2e^{-\frac{3}{5}}$ **47.** $3b^{-\frac{2}{7}}$ **48.** $5t^{-\frac{5}{3}}$

49. $9c^{-4}$ **50.** $10k^{-\frac{5}{4}}$

1. a **2.** r^2 **3.** $\sqrt[3]{s^4}$ **4.** $\sqrt[4]{p^5}$

5. 1 **6.** $\sqrt{m^7}$ **7.** $\frac{1}{\sqrt[5]{s}}$ **8.** $\sqrt[3]{j^8}$

9. 1 **10.** $\sqrt[6]{d}$ **11.** $\frac{1}{\sqrt[4]{d^5}}$ **12.** $\sqrt[10]{d^9}$

13. $\frac{1}{\sqrt[4]{t^3}}$ **14.** $\frac{6}{\sqrt{x^3}}$ **15.** $\frac{\sqrt[3]{y^4}}{2}$ **16.** $\sqrt[3]{z^7}$

17. $\sqrt[4]{a^5}$ **18.** $\frac{1}{\sqrt[4]{c}}$ **19.** $\frac{6}{\sqrt[6]{s^5}}$ **20.** $\frac{1}{2\sqrt{v}}$

21. $8\sqrt{x^3}$ **22.** $9\sqrt[3]{a^4}$ **23.** $64\sqrt[4]{b^3}$ **24.** $125c^2$

Chapter 2

1. $ab+ac$ **2.** $cd+ce$ **3.** $de+df$ **4.** $ef+eg$

5. $ab+2a$ **6.** $bc+5b$ **7.** $de+9d$ **8.** $5e+ef$

9. g^2+gh **10.** $hk+h^2$ **11.** $2j+2k$ **12.** $5p+5q$

13. $6m+6n$ **14.** $7p+7r$ **15.** $11w+11s$ **16.** $9e+9v$

17. $4e+24$ **18.** $8x+32$ **19.** $3t+27$ **20.** $12e+36$

21. $7p+21$ **22.** $10a+50$ **23.** $8w+24$ **24.** $10r+15$

25. $32c+8$ **26.** $45h+36$ **27.** $24+32c$ **28.** $5+45p$

29. $12b+18e$ **30.** $36x+42$ **31.** $4a^2+8a$ **32.** $3x^2+18x$

33. $2g^2+6g$ **34.** $5t^2+40t$ **35.** $8d^2+40cd$ **36.** $12y^2+18xy$

37. $4b+22$ **38.** $5d+16$ **39.** $8g+18$ **40.** $7h+41$

41. $7c+14$ **42.** $8k+30$ **43.** $7f+81$ **44.** $3d+47$

45. $5a^2+27a$ **46.** $14c^2+10c$ **47.** $8s^2+6s$ **48.** $16a^2+38a$

1. $ab-ac$ **2.** $cd-ce$ **3.** $de-df$

4. $ef-eg$ **5.** $ab-3a$ **6.** $bc-2b$

7. $de - d$

8. $9e - ef$

9. $g^2 - 2g$

10. $3h - h^2$

11. $-2j - 2e$

12. $-4p - 4w$

13. $-8m - 8n$

14. $-p - r$

15. $-2w - 2s$

16. $-6e - 6v$

17. $-2e - 12$

18. $-7x - 28$

19. $-3t - 27$

20. $-20e - 60$

21. $-2p + 6$

22. $-10a + 50$

23. $-6w + 6$

24. $-35r + 14$

25. $-6c + 3$

26. $-33h + 33$

27. $-3a^2 + 12a$

28. $-6b^2 - 6bp$

29. $-2c^2 + 3c$

30. $36x^2 - 42x$

31. $-2a^2 - 4a$

32. $-x + 6$

33. $-6g^2 + 9g$

34. $-4t^2 - 6t$

35. $5d^2 - 25cd$

36. $-12y + 18y^2$

37. $b - 1$

38. $3 - d$

39. $4g - 6$

40. $11 - 2h$

41. $2 - c$

42. $-5k$

43. $-2f - 30$

44. -44

45. $-2a^2 + 13a$

46. $-6e^2 - e$

47. $-s^2 + 8s$

48. 16

Exercise 1.3   Page 14

1. $5a + 14$

2. $7b + 7$

3. $12c - 55$

4. $9d + 42$

5. $8e + 24$

6. $14f + 66$

7. $13g + 6$

8. $7h^2 + 15h$

9. $14j^2 - 12j$

10. $3k^2 + 20k + 10$

11. $5m^2 - 3m + 8$

12. $7n^2 - 25n + 30$

13. $4p - 9$

14. $5q + 9$

15. $2r + 7$

16. $s - 2$

17. $6t + 67$

18. $8u + 33$

19. $-v - 26$

20. $2w + 1$

21. $7x - 6$

22. $2y^2 - 9y + 12$

23. $4z^2 + 33z + 24$

24. $5a - 11$

Exercise 2.1   Page 15

1. $a^2 + 5a + 6$

2. $b^2 + 6b + 5$

3. $c^2 + 9c + 18$

4. $d^2 + 2d + 1$

5. $e^2 + 6e + 9$

6. $f^2 + 8f + 12$

7. $g^2 + 11g + 30$

8. $h^2 + 12h + 27$

9. $j^2 + 9j + 14$

10. $k^2 + 12k + 35$

11. $m^2 + 9m + 8$

12. $n^2 + 2n + 1$

13. $p^2 + 4p + 4$

14. $q^2 + 10q + 25$

15. $r^2 + 16r + 64$

16. $s^2 + 14s + 33$

17. $2t^2 + 7t + 3$

18. $3u^2 + 14u + 15$

19. $5v^2 + 7v + 2$

20. $6w^2 + 11w + 4$

21. $x^2 + xz + yx + zy$

22. $6x^2 + 4xz + 9xy + 6yz$

23. $15x^2 + 38xy + 24y^2$

24. $35x^2 + 21xz + 20xy + 12yz$

Exercise 2.2   Page 16

1. $a^2 + a - 2$

2. $b^2 - 2b - 15$

3. $c^2 + 4c - 12$

4. $d^2 - 2d - 3$

5. $e^2 - e - 12$

6. $f^2 - 3f - 10$

7. $g^2 - g - 42$

8. $h^2 + 2h - 3$

9. $j^2 - 4$

10. $k^2 - 16$

11. $m^2 + m - 30$

12. $n^2 - 9$

13. $p^2 - 5p - 24$

14. $q^2 - 4q - 21$

15. $r^2 - r - 72$

16. $s^2 - 5s - 50$

17. $t^2 - 64$

18. $u^2 - v^2$

19. $2v^2 - 3vw - 2w^2$

20. $w^2 - wx - 6x^2$

21. $12x^2 - 7xy - 10y^2$

22. $2y^2 - 4yz + 2y - 4z$

23. $6x^2 - 9xz + 4xy - 6yz$

24. $8x^2 + 8xy - 6yz - 6xz$

Exercise 2.3   Page 16

1. $a^2 - 4a + 3$

2. $b^2 - 7b + 10$

3. $c^2 - 3c + 2$

4. $d^2 - 5d + 6$

5. $e^2 - 9e + 20$

6. $f^2 - 11f + 30$

7. $g^2 - 9g + 14$

8. $h^2 - 10h + 9$

9. $j^2 - 4j + 4$

10. $k^2 - 10k + 25$

11. $m^2 - 6m + 9$

12. $n^2 - 12n + 36$

13. $p^2 - 9p + 8$

14. $q^2 - 17q + 70$

15. $r^2 - 12r + 27$

16. $s^2 - 12s + 20$

17. $t^2 - 12t + 32$

18. $u^2 - 2uv + v^2$

19. $v^2 - 3vw + 2w^2$

20. $2w^2 - 7xw + 3x^2$

21. $5x^2 - 17xy + 6y^2$

22. $2y^2 - 4yz - 3y + 6z$

23. $10x^2 - 15xz - 4yz + 6yz$

24. $-14x^2 + 14xy - 6yz + 6xz$

Exercise 2.4   Page 17

1. $a^2 + 2ab + b^2$

2. $b^2 + 2bc + c^2$

3. $c^2 - 2cd + d^2$

4. $d^2 + 2d + 1$

5. $e^2 - 2e + 1$

6. $f^2 + 4f + 4$

7. $g^2 - 4g + 4$

8. $h^2 + 6h + 9$

9. $j^2 - 6j + 9$

10. $k^2 + 8k + 16$

11. $m^2 - 8m + 16$

12. $n^2 - 10n + 25$

13. $p^2 + 12p + 36$

14. $q^2 + 20q + 100$

15. $r^2 - 14r + 49$

16. $s^2 + 10s + 25$

17. $16 - 8x + x^2$

18. $25 + 10y + y^2$

19. $4x^2 - 16x + 16$

20. $9y^2 + 12xy + 4z^2$

Exercise 2.5   Page 17

1. $4a - 4$

2. $b^2 - b - 6$

3. $c^2 + 12c + 36$

4. $d^2 - 2d - 3$

5. $2e^2 + 8e$

6. $f^2 - 10f + 25$

7. $g^2 - 36$

8. $4h^2 - 4h$

9. $j^2 + 4j + 4$

10. $k^2 - 25$

11. $m^2 - m - 42$

12. $n^2 - 1$

13. $p^2 - 3p - 40$

14. $q^2 + 2q - 63$

15. $r^2 - 2r - 80$

16. $s^2 + 4s - 5$

17. $t^2 - 100$

18. $u^2 - 49$

19. $a^2 + 3a - 10$

20. $b^2 + 5b + 6$

21. $c^2 - 13c + 40$

22. $d^2 - d - 72$

23. $e^2 - 20e + 100$

24. $f^2 + 9f - 36$

25. $g^2 + 16g + 55$

26. $h^2 - 36$

27. $j^2 + 22j + 120$

28. $k^2 - 25$

29. $m^2 + 15m + 56$

30. $-n^2 + 16n - 60$

31. $2v^2 - 3vw - 2w^2$

32. $w^2 - xw - 6x^2$

33. $12x^2 - 7xy - 10y^2$

34. $2y^2 - 4yz + 2y - 4z$

35. $6x^2 + 9xz + 4xy + 6yz$

36. $8xy + 8x^2 - 6yz - 6xz$

Exercise 3.1   Page 18

1. $a^2 + \frac{3}{2}a + \frac{1}{2}$

2. $b^2 + \frac{3}{2}b - 1$

3. $c^2 - \frac{1}{4}$

4. $d^2 + \frac{2}{3}d + \frac{1}{9}$

5. $e^2 - \frac{7}{6}e + \frac{1}{3}$

6. $f^2 - \frac{5}{12}f - \frac{1}{6}$

7. $g^2 + \frac{27}{20}g + \frac{9}{20}$

8. $h^2 - \frac{13}{15}h + \frac{2}{15}$

9. $j^2 - \frac{1}{20}j - \frac{3}{40}$

10. $2k^2 - \frac{1}{12}k - \frac{1}{24}$

11. $\frac{3}{2}m^2 - \frac{86}{45}m + \frac{2}{15}$

12. $\frac{1}{5}n^2 + \frac{7}{10}n - \frac{3}{16}$

13. $3p^2 + \frac{51}{20}p + \frac{9}{20}$

14. $2q^2 - \frac{6}{5}q + \frac{7}{40}$

15. $2r^2 - \frac{22}{15}r - \frac{1}{6}$

16. $s^2 - 2 + \frac{1}{s^2}$

17. $t^2 - 3 + \frac{2}{t^2}$

18. $u^2 + \frac{1}{2} - \frac{1}{2u^2}$

19. $v^2 + 5 + \frac{6}{v^2}$

20. $\frac{w^2}{2} - 7 - \frac{w}{8} + \frac{7}{4w}$

21. $\frac{2}{x^2} + 1 - x^2$

1. $x^5 + x^3$
2. $y^4 + y^3$
3. $w + w^3$
4. $v^3 + 1$
5. $z^2 - z^4 - z^3 + z^5$
6. $u^2 - 1 + u^3 - u$
7. $a + \sqrt{a^3}$
8. $\sqrt{b^3} + 1$
9. $c + \sqrt[3]{c^5}$
10. $\sqrt{d} + \sqrt[4]{d^7}$
11. $e^2 - 2\sqrt{e^3} + e$
12. $f^2 - f$
13. $g^2 + g\sqrt{a} + \frac{g}{\sqrt{a}} + 1$
14. $h^2 + \sqrt[3]{h^2} - \sqrt[3]{h^4} + 1$
15. $j^2 - \sqrt{j} + j^3 - \sqrt{j^3}$
16. $k^3 + \sqrt{k^3} - \sqrt{k} - \frac{1}{k}$
17. $\sqrt{m^5} - m$
18. $\sqrt{n^5} - \sqrt[6]{n^{13}}$
19. $\sqrt[3]{p^7} - \sqrt[6]{p^{11}}$
20. $\sqrt[3]{q^4} + \frac{1}{\sqrt[6]{q}}$
21. $\sqrt{r^5} + 1$
22. $s - 2 + s^{-1}$
23. $\sqrt[3]{t^2} - 2 + \frac{1}{\sqrt[3]{t^2}}$
24. $\sqrt[3]{v^4} - 2 + \frac{1}{\sqrt[3]{v^4}}$

1. $a^3 + 3a^2 + 3a + 1$
2. $b^3 + 3b^2 + 3b + 2$
3. $c^3 + 5c^2 + 7c + 2$
4. $d^3 + 6d^2 + 8d + 3$
5. $e^3 - 2e^2 - 5e - 12$
6. $f^3 - 2f^2 - 16f + 5$
7. $g^3 - 5g^2 + 7g - 2$
8. $h^3 - 4h^2 - 6h - 1$
9. $j^3 - j^2 - 7j + 15$
10. $k^3 - 18k + 8$
11. $m^3 - 24m - 5$
12. $n^3 - 4n^2 - n + 12$
13. $p^3 + 8p^2 + 14p - 3$
14. $q^3 + 2q^2 + 3q + 18$
15. $r^3 + r^2 - 15r + 9$
16. $2s^3 + 2s^2 - 11s + 3$
17. $6t^3 + 31t^2 + 43t + 8$
18. $12u^3 - 2u^2 - 7u + 2$
19. $2v^3 - 12v^2 + 8v + 2$
20. $4w^3 - 14w^2 + 7w - 3$
21. $15x^3 + 34x^2 - 6x - 35$
22. $10y^3 - 31y^2 - 32y + 63$
23. $15z^3 + 40z^2 - 3z - 8$
24. $15z^3 - 9z^2 - 25z + 15$

1. $a^3 + 10a^2 + 31a + 30$
2. $b^3 + 5b^2 + 8b + 4$
3. $c^3 + 11c^2 + 34c + 24$
4. $d^3 - 7d^2 + 7d + 15$
5. $e^3 - 6e^2 - 7e + 60$
6. $f^3 - 9f^2 + 23f - 15$
7. $g^3 - g^2 - 22g + 40$
8. $h^3 + h^2 - h - 1$
9. $j^3 - 5j^2 - 29j + 105$
10. $k^3 - 13k^2 + 50k - 56$
11. $m^3 - 13m^2 + 31m + 45$
12. $n^3 + 2n^2 - 51n + 108$
13. $p^3 - 6p^2 + 12p - 8$
14. $q^3 + 6q^2 - 9q - 54$
15. $r^3 - 15r^2 + 75r - 125$
16. $s^3 + 12s^2 + 48s + 64$
17. $t^3 - 18t^2 + 108t - 216$
18. $2u^3 + u^2 - 13u + 6$
19. $2v^3 + 2v^2 - 2v - 2$
20. $w^3 - 5w^2 + 3w + 9$
21. $4x^3 - 20x^2 - 61x + 35$
22. $8y^3 - 44y^2 + 78y - 45$
23. $27z^3 + 108z^2 + 144z + 64$
24. $z^5 - 3z^4 - 10z^3 + 30z^2 + 25z - 75$

Chapter 3

1. $3(a + 1)$
2. $4(b - 1)$
3. $5(c - 3)$
4. $6(c + 2)$
5. $2(5e - 1)$
6. $9(2f + 1)$
7. $2(3g - 1)$
8. $2(4h - 3)$
9. $3(4i + 5)$
10. $9(2j - 3)$
11. $4(4k - 3)$
12. $10(5m - 1)$
13. $4(3 - n)$
14. $5(3 + 2p)$
15. $8(1 - 3q)$
16. $12(2r - 3)$
17. $4(8s - 5)$
18. $15(8t - 3)$
19. $2(3v - 7u)$
20. $8(w - 4x)$
21. $5(5x + 6y)$

22. $9(5x - 2y + 3z)$
23. $4(8x - 12y + 15z)$
24. $10(10a - 35b + 8c)$

1. $x(3 + 4b)$
2. $y(4 - c)$
3. $c(1 - 2t)$
4. $r(5 + 6a)$
5. $t(10 - 7d)$
6. $b(3a + 2c)$
7. $x(5y - 3z)$
8. $bc(8a - 3d)$
9. $a(5a - 4)$
10. $v(v - 7)$
11. $w(3w + 2x)$
12. $z(z - 3x)$
13. $abc(5a - 1)$
14. $km(k - n)$
15. $d(c^2 - 2e)$
16. $g(11gh - 3e + 2)$
17. $cd(b - 2 + 3e)$
18. $vwx(5v - x)$
19. $abc(b + a)$
20. $abc^2(a + 1)$
21. $xy^2z(x + 1 - z)$
22. $cde(e + 2d - cde)$
23. $pr(qr + 2p - 5pqr)$
24. $st(t + s - stu)$

1. $2b(a + 3)$
2. $5x(y - 3)$
3. $4g(1 + 3h)$
4. $2c(3a + 4)$
5. $3m(4n + 5)$
6. $3r(7g - 4)$
7. $2t(s - 6v)$
8. $3w(3w + 4)$
9. $5a(a - 4)$
10. $5n(5n - 2)$
11. $2a(3a + 4)$
12. $10w(3w - 2)$
13. $8a(4a - 3)$
14. $9n(2n - 1)$
15. $3a(a - 2)$
16. $4d(10d - 3)$
17. $2c(15 + 2c)$
18. $5bc(5c - 2b)$
19. $3ef(3f + 4e)$
20. $8y(3y + 1)$
21. $5xy(xy + 4y - 2x)$
22. $4de(2e + 3d - 4de)$
23. $2rst(3t + r - 4rt)$
24. $7tu(t + 4 - 2tu)$
25. $5abc(a - 4)$
26. $9m(1 - 3m)$
27. $16c(2 + c)$
28. $3gh(4 - 6g + 3h)$
29. $2cde(15ce - c + 4e)$
30. $6gr(7r - 2g)$
31. $6a(7 - 5a)$
32. $2wxy^2(7w + 16x)$
33. $7uv(4 + 5v - 8u)$
34. $3d(3e^2 + 4cd - 5c^2de^2)$
35. $3cde(4e + 6d - 5cde)$
36. $2rs(4r - 13rst + 9st)$

1. $(x + y)(x - y)$
2. $(y + z)(y - z)$
3. $(a + b)(a - b)$
4. $(v + u)(v - u)$
5. $(c + d)(c - d)$
6. $(m + n)(m - n)$
7. $(x + 3)(x - 3)$
8. $(x + 5)(x - 5)$
9. $(x + 7)(x - 7)$
10. $(x + 1)(x - 1)$
11. $(x + 2)(x - 2)$
12. $(x + 4)(x - 4)$
13. $(x + 6)(x - 6)$
14. $(3 + x)(3 - x)$
15. $(x + 8)(x - 8)$
16. $(1 + x)(1 - x)$
17. $(x + 7)(x - 7)$
18. $(6 + x)(6 - x)$
19. $(10 + x)(10 - x)$
20. $(x + 9)(x - 9)$
21. $(x + 12)(x - 12)$
22. $(x + 13)(x - 13)$
23. $(11 + x)(11 - x)$
24. $(x + 20)(x - 20)$
25. $(4 + 3x)(4 - 3x)$
26. $(2x + 5)(2x - 5)$
27. $(4x + 11)(4x - 11)$
28. $(6x + 13)(6x - 13)$
29. $(1 + 5x)(1 - 5x)$
30. $(9x + 2)(9x - 2)$

1. $5(x + 1)(x - 1)$
2. $2(x + 3)(x - 3)$
3. $3(x + 2)(x - 2)$
4. $5(x + 3)(x - 3)$
5. $7(x + 2)(x - 2)$
6. $3(x + 3)(x - 3)$
7. $10(x + 3)(x - 3)$
8. $11(x + 2)(x - 2)$

9. $5(x+5)(x-5)$

10. $\frac{1}{2}(x+2)(x-2)$

11. $\frac{1}{4}(x+6)(x-6)$

12. $4(x+2)(x-2)$

13. $4(x+3)(x-3)$

14. $2(3+x)(3-x)$

15. $\frac{1}{3}(x+3)(x-3)$

16. $4(5+x)(5-x)$

17. $4(x+10)(x-10)$

18. $25(x+2)(x-2)$

19. $25(4+x)(4-x)$

20. $\frac{1}{3}(x+9)(x-9)$

21. $2(x+12)(x-12)$

22. $\frac{1}{5}(x+5)(x-5)$

23. $\frac{1}{2}(6+x)(6-x)$

24. $2(x+7)(x-7)$

Exercise 2.3   Page 25

1. $(x+1)(x+1)$
2. $(x+3)(x+1)$
3. $(x+2)(x+1)$
4. $(x+3)(x+2)$
5. $(x+4)(x+1)$
6. $(x+2)(x+2)$
7. $(x+5)(x+2)$
8. $(x+6)(x+1)$
9. $(x+4)(x+2)$
10. $(x+9)(x+1)$
11. $(x+8)(x+1)$
12. $(x+3)(x+3)$
13. $(x+5)(x+3)$
14. $(x+4)(x+3)$
15. $(x+6)(x+2)$
16. $(x+15)(x+1)$
17. $(x+10)(x+2)$
18. $(x+12)(x+1)$
19. $(x+6)(x+4)$
20. $(x+6)(x+6)$
21. $(x+8)(x+3$
22. $(x+20)(x+5)$
23. $(x+5)(x+5)$
24. $(x+15)(x+2)$

Exercise 2.4   Page 26

1. $(x-1)(x-1)$
2. $(x-3)(x-1)$
3. $(x-4)(x-1)$
4. $(x-6)(x-1)$
5. $(x-2)(x-2)$
6. $(x-4)(x-3)$
7. $(x-10)(x-1)$
8. $(x-6)(x-2)$
9. $(x-3)(x-5)$
10. $(x-6)(x-4)$
11. $(x-8)(x-4)$
12. $(x-14)(x-2)$
13. $(x-12)(x-2)$
14. $(x-12)(x-2)$
15. $(x-5)(x-5)$
16. $(x-9)(x-3)$
17. $(x-5)(x-4)$
18. $(x-20)(x-1)$
19. $(x-20)(x-2)$
20. $(x-16)(x-2)$
21. $(x-6)(x-7)$
22. $(x-16)(x-4)$
23. $(x-5)(x-6)$
24. $(x-16)(x-5)$

Exercise 2.5   Page 26

1. $(x-2)(x+1)$
2. $(x+3)(x-1)$
3. $(x-4)(x+1)$
4. $(x-6)(x+1)$
5. $(x+4)(x-2)$
6. $(x+4)(x-3)$
7. $(x-6)(x+2)$
8. $(x-12)(x+2)$
9. $(x+8)(x-2)$
10. $(x-12)(x+1)$
11. $(x+2)(x-1)$
12. $(x+6)(x-4)$
13. $(x+5)(x-1)$
14. $(x+9)(x-4)$
15. $(x+5)(x-3)$
16. $(x-5)(x+4)$
17. $(x+10)(x-1)$
18. $(x+8)(x-3)$
19. $(x-8)(x+5)$
20. $(x-25)(x+4)$
21. $(x-12)(x+3)$
22. $(x+15)(x-3)$
23. $(x+10)(x-3)$
24. $(x-16)(x+4)$
25. $(4+x)(3-x)$
26. $(5-x)(3+x)$
27. $(8+x)(1-x)$
28. $(8-x)(3+x)$
29. $(9+x)(4-x)$
30. $(20-x)(6+x)$

Exercise 2.6   Page 27

1. $(x+3)(x+2)$
2. $(x+1)(x-9)$
3. $(x-2)(x+7)$
4. $(x-6)(x-2)$
5. $(x-8)(x-3)$
6. $(x-9)(x+4)$
7. $(x-6)(x-3)$
8. $(x-7)(x-6)$
9. $(x-4)(x-4)$
10. $(x+6)(x-5)$
11. $(x-8)(x+2)$
12. $(x-6)(x-4)$
13. $(x-8)(x+7)$
14. $(x+12)(x+3)$
15. $(x-6)(x+2)$
16. $(x+14)(x-1)$
17. $(x+8)(x+4)$
18. $(x+50)(x-2)$
19. $(x-12)(x+2)$
20. $(x+7)(x-6)$
21. $(x+9)(x+9)$
22. $(x-16)(x-4)$
23. $(x-25)(x+8)$
24. $(x-9)(x+5)$
25. $(x-8)(x+6)$
26. $(x+16)(x-5)$
27. $(x+13)(x+6)$
28. $(x-12)(x+5)$
29. $(x+9)(x-8)$
30. $(x-15)(x+2)$

Exercise 2.7   Page 27

1. $(2x+1)(x+3)$
2. $(3x-1)(x-4)$
3. $(5x+1)(x-3)$
4. $(2x-3)(x-2)$
5. $(2x+5)(x-3)$
6. $(3x-2)(x+3)$
7. $(2x+1)(x-2)$
8. $(5x-2)(x+1)$
9. $(3x+1)(x-4)$
10. $(2x+1)(x+5)$
11. $(3x-1)(x+2)$
12. $(5x-3)(x-2)$
13. $(4x-1)(x+7)$
14. $(5x+4)(x-1)$
15. $(3x-5)(x-1)$
16. $(2x+7)(2x+1)$
17. $(6x-1)(x-5)$
18. $(8x+3)(x+1)$
19. $(7x-2)(x+3)$
20. $(3x+7)(2x-3)$
21. $(4x+3)(x-4)$
22. $(5x-7)(x+2)$
23. $(2x-9)(2x+3)$
24. $(3x+5)(2x+5)$
25. $(2x-7)(2x+5)$
26. $(8x+5)(x-5)$
27. $(4x+3)(3x-2)$
28. $(6x-7)(x+2)$
29. $(6x+5)(2x-3)$
30. $(3x-8)(4x+3)$

Exercise 2.8A   Page 28

1. $2x(x+3)$
2. $x(x-4)$
3. $3(x-1)(x+1)$
4. $(x-6)(x+4)$
5. $2(x+1)(x-4)$
6. $(x+3)(x+4)$
7. $(x+3)(x-3)$
8. $10x(x+1)$
9. $(x+1)(x+1)$
10. $9x(x+7)$
11. $3(x+2)(x-2)$
12. $(x-10)(x-1)$
13. $4(4-x)(4+x)$
14. $(6+x)(3-x)$
15. $(x+1)(x+13)$
16. $7xy(x+2)$
17. $2(x-10)(x+2)$
18. $3(3+x)(3-x)$
19. $6xy(2x^2z+3)$
20. $3(x-3)(x+1)$
21. $12x(1+x)(1-x)$
22. $4(x-2)(x-2)$
23. $3(5-x)(3+x)$
24. $3(x^2+1)(x-1)(x+1)$

Exercise 2.8B   Page 28

1. $2x(x+4)$
2. $x(x-16)$
3. $3(x-3)(x+3)$
4. $(x-8)(x-1)$
5. $2(x+1)(x-3)$
6. $(3x-2)(x+3)$
7. $(x+1)(x-1)$
8. $5x(x+2)$
9. $(3x+5)(x-1)$
10. $12x(2x+5)$
11. $(x-2)(x+6)$
12. $4(x-5)(x-2)$
13. $4(5-x)(5+x)$
14. $(4+x)(2-x)$
15. $(7x-6)(x+2)$
16. $4xy(xy+4y+3)$

107

17. $2(2x - 1)(x - 3)$
18. $2(8 + x)(8 - x)$
19. $5x(x - 5)(x + 5)$
20. $(x - 9)(x - 6)$
21. $12x(2 + x)(2 - x)$
22. $(2x - 9)(2x + 3)$
23. $(6 - x)(3 + x)$
24. $(5 - 3x)(6 + x)$

Exercise 3.1   Page 29

1. $(x + 1)(x + 2)(x - 1)$
2. $(x + 2)(x - 2)(x + 4)$
3. $(x - 1)^2(x + 3)$
4. $(x - 2)(x - 3)(x + 1)$
5. $(x^2 + 1)(x + 1)(x - 1)$
6. $(x - 5)(x + 2)(x + 1)$
7. $(x - 3)(x - 1)^2$
8. $(x + 2)(x + 4)(x - 1)$
9. $(x^2 + 4)(x + 2)(x - 2)$
10. $(x + 5)(x - 4)(x - 2)$
11. $(x - 1)^3$
12. $(2x - 1)(x - 2)(x + 3)$
13. $(x + 2)(x + 3)(x + 1)$
14. $(x + 5)(x - 2)(x - 4)$
15. $(x - 2)^3(x + 2)$
16. $(x^2 + 1)(x - 3)(x + 3)$
17. $(x^2 + 3)(x + 1)(x - 1)$
18. $(x + 3)(x - 1)(x + 2)$
19. $(x - 5)(x + 1)(x + 2)$
20. $(x - 2)(x - 1)^3$
21. $(x + 5)(x + 1)(x - 2)^2$
22. $(2x + 1)(x + 2)(x + 1)$
23. $(x + 4)(x - 3)(x + 3)$
24. $(x + 2)^2(x - 1)^2$
25. $(x + 1)(x + 2)(x - 2)$
26. $(x + 3)^2(x - 1)$
27. $(x - 1)(x + 1)(x - 3)^2$

Chapter 4

Exercise 1.1A   Page 32

1. $a = 2$
2. $b = 8$
3. $c = 2$
4. $d = 1$
5. $e = 16$
6. $f = 2$
7. $g = 5$
8. $h = 1$
9. $i = 20$
10. $j = 15$
11. $k = 1$
12. $l = 17$
13. $m = 5$
14. $n = 33$
15. $p = 15$
16. $q = 33$
17. $r = 47$
18. $s = 1$
19. $t = 4$
20. $u = 6$
21. $v = 1$
22. $w = 1$
23. $x = 6$
24. $y = 0$
25. $z = 25$
26. $a = 5$
27. $c = 42$
28. $w = 12$
29. $r = 5$
30. $t = -1$
31. $z = -2$
32. $a = -7$
33. $c = -10$
34. $x = -5$
35. $y = -8$
36. $u = -10$
37. $t = -7$
38. $w = -16$
39. $z = -15$
40. $b = -4$

Exercise 1.1B   Page 32

1. $a = 12$
2. $b = 16$
3. $c = 13$
4. $d = 17$
5. $e = 18$
6. $f = 4$
7. $g = 9$
8. $h = 9$
9. $i = 40$
10. $j = 21$
11. $k = 19$
12. $l = 20$
13. $m = 9$
14. $n = 18$
15. $p = 16$
16. $q = 27$
17. $r = 66$
18. $s = 31$
19. $t = 14$
20. $u = 5$
21. $v = 35$
22. $w = 37$
23. $x = 30$
24. $y = 54$
25. $z = 83$
26. $a = 58$
27. $c = 23$
28. $w = 30$
29. $r = 14$
30. $t = 1$
31. $z = 2$
32. $a = 11$
33. $c = -1$
34. $x = 23$
35. $y = -2$
36. $u = 0$
37. $t = -3$
38. $w = -6$
39. $z = -3$
40. $b = -7$

Exercise 1.2A   Page 33

1. $a = 3$
2. $b = 4$
3. $c = 1$
4. $d = 3$
5. $e = 3$
6. $f = 4$
7. $g = 5$
8. $h = 5$
9. $i = 4$
10. $j = 8$
11. $k = 4$
12. $l = 5$
13. $m = 5$
14. $n = 4$
15. $p = 5$
16. $q = 5$
17. $r = 2$
18. $s = 5$
19. $t = 1$
20. $u = 2$

21. $v = -2$
22. $w = -3$
23. $x = -6$
24. $y = -20$
25. $z = 6$
26. $a = -20$
27. $y = \frac{1}{2}$
28. $t = 5$
29. $r = -7$
30. $t = 0$
31. $m = -3$
32. $g = 20$
33. $d = \frac{1}{2}$
34. $c = -\frac{1}{2}$
35. $y = -5$
36. $v = \frac{1}{2}$
37. $t = 21$
38. $x = \frac{1}{3}$
39. $z = -\frac{1}{4}$
40. $p = -\frac{1}{2}$

Exercise 1.2B   Page 34

1. $a = 6$
2. $b = 10$
3. $c = 9$
4. $d = 8$
5. $e = 12$
6. $f = 20$
7. $g = 24$
8. $h = 10$
9. $i = 21$
10. $j = 8$
11. $k = -10$
12. $l = -10$
13. $m = -24$
14. $n = -5$
15. $p = -15$
16. $q = -18$
17. $r = 6$
18. $s = 8$
19. $t = 6$
20. $u = 6$

Exercise 1.3   Page 34

1. $a = 2$
2. $b = 5$
3. $c = 6$
4. $d = 9$
5. $e = 8$
6. $f = 6$
7. $g = 7$
8. $h = 3$
9. $i = 5$
10. $j = 6$
11. $k = 3$
12. $l = 0$
13. $m = 1$
14. $n = -1$
15. $p = -2$
16. $q = -4$
17. $r = 18$
18. $s = -2$
19. $t = -3$
20. $u = 6$
21. $v = 16$
22. $w = 0$
23. $x = 8$
24. $y = -10$
25. $z = 10$
26. $a = -2$
27. $y = -6$
28. $t = 5$
29. $t = 13$
30. $t = -13$
31. $m = 12$
32. $g = 48$
33. $d = \frac{1}{2}$
34. $c = 2$
35. $y = 2$
36. $v = -2$
37. $t = 10$
38. $x = 1$
39. $z = 3$
40. $p = 0$

Exercise 1.4   Page 35

1. $a = 3$
2. $b = 2$
3. $c = 11$
4. $d = 6$
5. $e = 7$
6. $f = 4$
7. $g = 3$
8. $h = 6$
9. $i = 5$
10. $j = 8$
11. $k = 6$
12. $l = -8$
13. $m = 2$
14. $n = 1$
15. $p = 5$
16. $q = -1$
17. $r = 2$
18. $s = -9$
19. $t = 6$
20. $u = 11$
21. $v = -6$
22. $w = -1$
23. $x = -12$
24. $y = 4$
25. $z = 4$
26. $b = 4$
27. $t = 6$
28. $t = -7$
29. $c = 2$
30. $r = -2$
31. $m = 0$
32. $g = -3$
33. $h = 10$
34. $d = 1$
35. $y = -5$
36. $v = 5$

Exercise 1.5   Page 36

1. $a = \frac{11}{4}$
2. $b = \frac{2}{3}$
3. $c = -\frac{3}{4}$
4. $d = \frac{24}{5}$
5. $e = -\frac{5}{3}$
6. $f = -\frac{7}{4}$
7. $g = \frac{1}{2}$
8. $h = \frac{19}{2}$
9. $i = -\frac{7}{3}$
10. $j = -\frac{29}{3}$
11. $k = \frac{21}{10}$
12. $l = -\frac{13}{3}$
13. $m = -\frac{1}{2}$
14. $n = -\frac{5}{4}$
15. $p = -\frac{1}{2}$
16. $q = -\frac{3}{2}$
17. $r = \frac{7}{4}$
18. $s = \frac{17}{2}$
19. $t = \frac{2}{3}$
20. $u = \frac{7}{3}$
21. $v = \frac{8}{3}$
22. $w = -\frac{15}{2}$
23. $x = \frac{5}{7}$
24. $y = \frac{19}{4}$
25. $x = 1$
26. $b = -\frac{1}{5}$
27. $u = \frac{1}{13}$
28. $r = \frac{3}{2}$
29. $x = \frac{-15}{4}$
30. $y = \frac{19}{5}$

Exercise 1.6A   Page 37

1. $a = 1$
2. $b = 5$
3. $c = 9$
4. $d = -3$
5. $e = -4$
6. $f = 0$
7. $g = 9$
8. $h = 12$
9. $i = -\frac{7}{4}$
10. $j = 11$
11. $k = -1$
12. $l = -5$
13. $m = 2$
14. $n = -\frac{11}{2}$
15. $p = -\frac{13}{3}$
16. $q = 8$
17. $r = 6$
18. $s = -18$
19. $t = -\frac{17}{2}$
20. $u = \frac{31}{5}$
21. $v = -\frac{51}{4}$
22. $w = -\frac{1}{7}$
23. $x = \frac{13}{12}$
24. $y = \frac{1}{2}$

Exercise 1.6B   Page 37

1. $m = 3$
2. $g = 35$
3. $h = 5$
4. $d = \frac{1}{3}$
5. $y = 8$
6. $v = 0$
7. $r = -\frac{26}{3}$
8. $t = \frac{14}{3}$
9. $z = \frac{89}{5}$
10. $x = -\frac{7}{4}$
11. $a = \frac{7}{2}$
12. $b = \frac{5}{2}$
13. $y = \frac{41}{4}$
14. $x = \frac{3}{4}$

Exercise 1.7   Page 38

1. $24p$
2. $25p$
3. £1.30
4. $55p$
5. $4.5\ mins$
6. $27kg$
7. $38kg$
8. $7km$
9. $15\ mins$
10. £12,000
11. $5\ mins$
12. $54km$
13. $2000g$
14. $21\ mins$
15. $41s\ secs$
16. $500g$
17. £4000
18. $x = 5cm$
19. $x = 7cm$
20. $x = 7cm$
21. $x = 4cm$
22. $x = 4cm$
23. $x = 6cm$
24. $x = 5cm$
25. $x = 5cm$

Exercise 1.8A   Page 40

1. $a > 3$
2. $b < 5$
3. $c \geq 4$
4. $d > 2$
5. $e \geq 5$
6. $f \leq 6$
7. $g > 4$
8. $h \leq 7$
9. $i > 6$
10. $j < 7$
11. $k \geq 6$
12. $l < 7$
13. $m \leq 15$
14. $n > 7$
15. $p < 6$
16. $q \geq 4$
17. $r < 3$
18. $s \leq 4$
19. $t > 0$
20. $u < 3$

Exercise 1.8B   Page 41

1. $a > 6$
2. $b \leq 16$
3. $c < 9$
4. $d \geq 18$
5. $e \leq 3$
6. $f > -1$
7. $g \geq -1$
8. $h < 11$
9. $i \geq -6$
10. $j > 7$
11. $k \leq -7$
12. $l > 13$
13. $m \leq 1$
14. $n > 4$
15. $p > -2$
16. $q \geq 5$
17. $r < -1$
18. $s \leq -1$
19. $t < 0$
20. $u \geq 5$

Exercise 1.8C   Page 41

1. $a < 2$
2. $b > 4$
3. $c \geq 9$
4. $d \leq 6$
5. $e > 9$
6. $f \leq 2$
7. $g < -1$
8. $h \geq 3$
9. $i \leq 5$
10. $j \geq -1$
11. $k > -6$
12. $l < 0$
13. $m \leq -1$
14. $n < -1$
15. $p \leq -2$
16. $q < 4$
17. $r < 6$
18. $s \geq -24$
19. $t > 2$
20. $u \leq 3$

Exercise 1.8D   Page 41

1. $a < 1$
2. $b \leq 7$
3. $c > 4$
4. $d \geq 7$
5. $e > 4$
6. $f < 1$
7. $g \leq 6$
8. $h > -18$
9. $i \leq 15$
10. $j > -6$
11. $k \leq -1$
12. $l < 5$
13. $m \leq 3$
14. $n > -3$
15. $p \leq 2$
16. $q < 4$

17. $r \geq 3$
18. $s < -3$

Exercise 2.1A   Page 42

1. $x = 15$
2. $x = 18$
3. $x = 7$
4. $x = 12$
5. $x = 33$
6. $x = 10$
7. $x = 48$
8. $x = 2$
9. $x = 2$
10. $x = 25$
11. $x = 30$
12. $x = \frac{3}{2}$
13. $x = 2$
14. $x = \frac{35}{4}$
15. $x = \frac{15}{2}$
16. $x = 3$
17. $x = \frac{1}{2}$
18. $x = \frac{3}{2}$
19. $x = \frac{1}{9}$
20. $x = \frac{5}{12}$

Exercise 2.1B   Page 43

1. $x = 12$
2. $x = 40$
3. $x = 0$
4. $x = 6$
5. $x = -2$
6. $x = \frac{10}{3}$
7. $x = 6$
8. $x = 20$
9. $x = 4$
10. $x = -\frac{15}{4}$
11. $x = \frac{2}{5}$
12. $x = -\frac{21}{2}$
13. $x = 1$
14. $x = -\frac{7}{4}$
15. $x = -\frac{9}{2}$
16. $x = 2$
17. $x = \frac{4}{7}$
18. $x = \frac{1}{3}$
19. $x = -\frac{5}{2}$
20. $x = \frac{1}{4}$

Exercise 2.1C   Page 43

1. $x = \frac{9}{2}$
2. $x = -3$
3. $x = 6$
4. $x = \frac{20}{3}$
5. $x = 6$
6. $x = -15$
7. $x = -1$
8. $x = 8$
9. $x = 7$
10. $x = -\frac{8}{7}$
11. $x = -83$
12. $x = 9$
13. $x = 20$
14. $x = 3$
15. $x = \frac{20}{3}$
16. $x = -20$
17. $x = 5$
18. $x = -\frac{34}{3}$
19. $x = \frac{9}{2}$
20. $x = \frac{15}{2}$
21. $x = -\frac{17}{21}$
22. $x = \frac{32}{9}$
23. $x = -\frac{25}{3}$
24. $x = 27$
25. $x = -1$
26. $x = \frac{92}{9}$
27. $x = \frac{135}{26}$
28. $x = 6$
29. $x = \frac{26}{11}$
30. $x = 8$

Exercise 2.2   Page 44

1. $a < -18$
2. $b \leq \frac{25}{2}$
3. $c > \frac{58}{5}$
4. $d \geq -\frac{24}{5}$
5. $e < \frac{37}{6}$
6. $f < -\frac{14}{3}$
7. $g \geq -\frac{5}{2}$
8. $h < 35$
9. $i \leq -\frac{48}{5}$
10. $j > -5$
11. $k \geq -\frac{5}{3}$
12. $l \leq 2$
13. $m > -\frac{6}{7}$
14. $n \leq -\frac{12}{5}$
15. $p < -\frac{7}{12}$
16. $q < \frac{20}{7}$
17. $r \leq 2$
18. $s < \frac{5}{11}$
19. $t > 7$
20. $u \geq 105$
21. $v \leq \frac{6}{13}$

Chapter 5

Exercise 1.1A   Page 46

1. 9
2. 8
3. -10
4. -15
5. -18
6. 7
7. 2
8. -8
9. 3
10. -13
11. 15
12. 15
13. 7
14. -1
15. -11
16. 30
17. 18
18. -3
19. 48
20. -70

1. 2 2. 5 3. 3 4. 2
5. -10 6. 10 7. 8 8. -60
9. 10 10. 2 11. 5 12. 45
13. 9 14. 4 15. -26 16. 26
17. 8 18. 5 19. 3 20. 3

1. 4 2. 9 3. -16 4. 10
5. 36 6. 16 7. 25 8. 100
9. 12 10. -16 11. 8 12. 16
13. 72 14. 1 15. 9 16. 8
17. 49 18. 36 19. 50 20. 61
21. 4 22. 5 23. 2 24. 10

1. $V = 50.3 \ units^3$ 2. $V = 141.4 \ units^3$
3. $V = 197.9 \ units^3$ 4. $V = 1885.0 \ units^3$
5. $V = 339.3 \ units^3$ 6. $V = 863.9 \ units^3$
7. $V = 9952.6 \ units^3$ 8. $V = 785.4 \ units^3$
9. $V = 113.1 \ units^3$ 10. $V = 16.8 \ units^3$
11. $V = 26.2 \ units^3$ 12. $V = 1900.7 \ units^3$
13. $V = 837.8 \ units^3$ 14. $V = 25.7 \ units^3$
15. $V = 235.6 \ units^3$ 16. $V = 54.5 \ units^3$
17. $V = 33.5 \ units^3$ 18. $V = 113.1 \ units^3$
19. $V = 2144.7 \ units^3$ 20. $V = 4188.8 \ units^3$
21. $V = 904.8 \ units^3$ 22. $V = 523.6 \ units^3$
23. $V = 7238.2 \ units^3$ 24. $V = 3053.6 \ units^3$
25. $A = 615.8 \ units^2$ 26. $A = 1520.5 \ units^2$
27. $A = 50.3 \ units^2$ 28. $A = 12.6 \ units^2$
29. $A = 2827.4 \ units^2$ 30. $A = 1017.9 \ units^2$
31. $A = 1256.6 \ units^2$ 32. $A = 1809.6 \ units^2$
33. $h = 19.1 \ units$ 34. $h = 2.7 \ units$
35. $h = 5.3 \ units$ 36. $h = 1.1 \ units$
37. $h = 14.3 \ units$ 38. $h = 11.8 \ units$
39. $h = 1.9 \ units$ 40. $h = 17.0 \ units$
41. $r = 4.6 \ units$ 42. $r = 5.2 \ units$
43. $r = 3.0 \ units$ 44. $r = 7.0 \ units$
45. $h = 3.1 \ units$ 46. $h = 5.9 \ units$
47. $h = 1.9 \ units$ 48. $h = 9.2 \ units$

1. $x = 0.2, x = -1.2$ 2. $x = 0.2, x = -2.2$
3. $x = 0.3, x = -1$ 4. $x = 0.6, x = -3.6$
5. $x = 1, x = 0.5$ 6. $x = -0.1, x = -2.5$
7. $x = -0.2, x = 1.5$ 8. $x = 0.5, x = 6.5$
9. $x = -0.4, x = 1.2$ 10. $x = 0.3, x = -4.8$
11. $x = -4.1, x = 0.1$ 12. $x = -6.7, x = 0.7$
13. $x = -0.2, x = -1.4$ 14. $x = -0.3, x = 2.8$
15. $x = 0.1, x = -1.2$

1. 8 2. 8 3. 5 4. -35
5. 10 6. 1 7. -51 8. 11
9. -27 10. -7 11. -23 12. -4

13. -20 14. 37 15. -2 16. -11
17. 13 18. 8 19. 9 20. $\frac{23}{20}$
21. 15 22. 22 23. 53 24. 35
25. $\frac{14}{17}$ 26. 5 27. 35 28. 34
29. 86 30. $-\frac{7}{4}$ 31. 8 32. -2
33. 5 34. 32 35. 13 36. $\frac{49}{3}$
37. 104 38. 85 39. 21 40. 69
41. -2 42. 5 43. $\frac{3}{4}$ 44. $-\frac{16}{9}$
45. 0 46. $-\frac{1}{18}$ 47. $\frac{25}{8}$ 48. $\frac{-2}{21}$

1. $6x + 5$ 2. $6x$
3. $14 - 24x$ 4. $13 - 24x$
5. $12 - 16x$ 6. $-16x - 11$
7. $45 - 24x$ 8. $10 - 24x$
9. $6x + 1$ 10. $6x - 8$
11. $9x - 8$ 12. $9x - 16$
13. $2x^2 + 7$ 14. $4x^2 - 4x + 5$
15. $6x^2 - 5$ 16. $12x^2 - 12x + 1$
17. $9x^4 - 12x^2 + 8$ 18. $3x^4 + 24x^2 + 46$
19. $\frac{2}{9x^2-1}$ 20. $\frac{2}{3x^2+17}$
21. $\frac{1}{3x-1}$ 22. $x^4 + 8x^2 + 20$
23. $4x - 3$ 24. $27x^4 - 36x^2 + 10$
25. $\frac{3x-6}{2x-3}$ 26. $\frac{9-3x}{8-2x}$
27. $\frac{3x-15}{2x-6}$ 28. $\frac{3x+6}{2x+7}$
29. $\frac{2x-4}{3x-7}$ 30. $\frac{2x-10}{3x-19}$
31. $\frac{2x+4}{3x+3}$ 32. $\frac{6-2x}{7-3x}$
33. $\frac{3-x}{2x-4}$ 34. $\frac{x-5}{14-2x}$
35. $\frac{x-2}{5-2x}$ 36. $\frac{4x-8}{11-5x}$

1. 3 2. 8 3. $-\frac{11}{3}$ 4. $\frac{1}{8}$
5. 0 6. $\frac{1}{25}$ 7. $\frac{1}{10}$ 8. $\frac{17}{3}$
9. 21 10. 80 11. -21 12. -9
13. 14 14. 38 15. 49 16. 234
17. 198 18. 352 19. $\frac{1}{17}$ 20. $\frac{2}{15}$
21. $-\frac{1}{11}$ 22. 123 23. $-\frac{2}{17}$ 24. $\frac{1}{42}$

Chapter 6

1. $x = 2, y = 1$ 2. $x = 1, y = -2$
3. $x = 4, y = -3$ 4. $x = 2, y = 2$
5. $x = 6, y = -2$ 6. $x = 5, y = 6$
7. $x = 1, y = -1$ 8. $x = 9, y = -2$
9. $x = 7, y = 5$ 10. $x = -14, y = -18$
11. $x = -2, y = 1$ 12. $x = -18, y = 7$

13. $x = -4, y = -1$ **14.** $x = -14, y = -3$

15. $x = -3, y = 3$ **16.** $x = -2, y = 1$

17. $x = -15, y = 7$ **18.** $x = -4, y = -1$

19. $x = -4, y = 3$ **20.** $x = -3, y = 10$

21. $x = -5, y = 20$ **22.** $x = -0.5, y = 2$

23. $x = -3, y = 15$ **24.** $x = -3, y = 12$

25. $x = 0.5, y = -2$ **26.** $x = 3, y = 8$

27. $x = -4, y = 7$ **28.** $x = -0.5, y = 13$

29. $x = 1, y = 14$ **30.** $x = -0.5, y = 2$

31. $x = 0.5, y = 0.5$ **32.** $x = 0.25, y = 4$

Exercise 2.1B Page 55

1. $x = 1, y = 1$ **2.** $x = 1, y = -1$

3. $x = 3, y = 2$ **4.** $x = 1, y = 2$

5. $x = 1, y = 3$ **6.** $x = 4, y = 1$

7. $x = 2, y = -1$ **8.** $x = 5, y = -2$

9. $x = 6, y = 2$ **10.** $x = -1, y = -6$

11. $x = -3, y = -2$ **12.** $x = 3, y = -2$

13. $x = -5, y = -1$ **14.** $x = -2, y = -2$

15. $x = -5, y = 3$ **16.** $x = -2, y = 1$

17. $x = 3, y = 1$ **18.** $x = 2, y = 2$

19. $x = 7, y = -0.5$ **20.** $x = 0.5, y = 2$

Exercise 2.2A   Page 57

1. $x = 2, y = 1$ **2.** $x = 2, y = 2$

3. $x = 1, y = 2$ **4.** $x = 3, y = 2$

5. $x = 2, y = -3$ **6.** $x = 3, y = -2$

7. $x = -2, y = 1$ **8.** $x = 3, y = -2$

9. $x = 4, y = 2$ **10.** $x = -1, y = -3$

11. $x = -2, y = -2$ **12.** $x = 4, y = -1$

13. $x = -5, y = 6$ **14.** $x = 2, y = -2$

15. $x = 2, y = -3$ **16.** $x = 2, y = 1$

17. $x = 2, y = -10$ **18.** $x = 8, y = 4$

19. $x = 5, y = 6$ **20.** $x = 3, y = -1$

21. $x = -2, y = -5$ **22.** $x = 8, y = -4$

23. $x = 3, y = -2$ **24.** $x = 2, y = -0.5$

Exercise 2.2B   Page 57

1. $x = 1, y = 1$ **2.** $x = 2, y = 2$

3. $x = 1, y = 2$ **4.** $x = 3, y = 2$

5. $x = 2, y = -3$ **6.** $x = 3, y = -2$

7. $x = -2, y = 1$ **8.** $x = 3, y = -2$

9. $x = 4, y = 2$ **10.** $x = -1, y = -3$

11. $x = -2, y = -2$ **12.** $x = 4, y = -1$

13. $x = -5, y = 6$ **14.** $x = 2, y = -2$

15. $x = 2, y = -3$ **16.** $x = 2, y = 1$

17. $x = 2, y = -10$ **18.** $x = 5, y = 4$

19. $x = 5, y = 6$ **20.** $x = 3, y = -1$

Exercise 2.2C   Page 58

1. $x = 2, y = 3$ **2.** $x = 1, y = 3$

3. $x = 4, y = 2$ **4.** $x = 3, y = -2$

5. $x = -2, y = 1$ **6.** $x = 5, y = 2$

7. $x = -3, y = 2$ **8.** $x = 5, y = -1$

9. $x = 6, y = 1$ **10.** $x = -4, y = -2$

11. $x = -3, y = 4$ **12.** $x = 2, y = -5$

13. $x = -6, y = 6$ **14.** $x = 3, y = -1$

15. $x = 5, y = -0.5$ **16.** $x = 3, y = 2$

17. $x = 2, y = -2.5$ **18.** $x = 6, y = 1.5$

19. $x = 2.5, y = 3$ **20.** $x = 3.5, y = -2$

21. $x = -0.5, y = -2.5$ **22.** $x = 4, y = -2$

23. $x = 6, y = -3.5$ **24.** $x = 2.25, y = -0.5$

Exercise 2.2D   Page 59

1. $x = 1, y = 3$ **2.** $x = 2, y = 3$

3. $x = 3, y = 4$ **4.** $x = 4, y = -1$

5. $x = -2, y = -1$ **6.** $x = 3, y = 2$

7. $x = -3, y = 1$ **8.** $x = 5, y = -2$

9. $x = 2, y = -1$ **10.** $x = 6, y = -2$

11. $x = 3, y = 4$ **12.** $x = 2, y = 3$

13. $x = 4, y = 3$ **14.** $x = 5, y = 6$

15. $x = 4, y = 7$ **16.** $x = 3, y = -2$

17. $x = 2, y = -2$ **18.** $x = 6, y = 3$

19. $x = 5, y = 3$ **20.** $x = 0.5, y = -2$

21. $x = 2.5, y = -1.5$ **22.** $x = 4, y = 0.5$

23. $x = 5, y = -2.5$ **24.** $x = 3.5, y = -0.5$

25. $x = 1, y = -1.5$ **26.** $x = 2, y = 0.5$

27. $x = 4, y = 2$ **28.** $x = 3, y = 2$

29. $x = 3, y = -0.5$ **30.** $x = 5, y = 1$

31. $x = 1, y = 2$ **32.** $x = 6, y = -1$

Exercise 2.3A   Page 60

1. Pencil £0.12, Rubber £0.20

2. Standard £5.50, Superior £8.50

3. 150 Standard, 50 Business tickets

4. 1 text £0.05, 1 minute £0.12

5. Apple £0.25, Orange £0.30

6. Strip £1, Individual £0.35

7. 45 Standard, 12 Extra Legroom

8. 20 £1 coins and 30 £2 coins

9. 7 correctly and 8 incorrectly

10. Bed £40, Breakfast £8

11. Ice cream £3.50, Waffle £4.50

12. Text £0.03, Call £0.20

13 Chocolate bar £0.55, Crisps £0.60

14. 120 50p coins and 100 20p coins

15. Coffee £2.50, Cake £1.20

16. 40 First Class and 280 Standard Class

17. Superior £70, Standard £55

18. Pen £0.75, pencil £0.45

19. £26.30

20. Correct 5 points awarded, incorrect 3 points deducted

21. Text £0.05, Call £0.15

22. £9.40

23. Standard £8.60, Superior £10.20

24. £13.30

Exercise 2.3B   Page 63

1. $x = 2, y = 1$ **2.** $x = 2, y = 2$

3. $x = 3, y = 2$ **4.** $x = 3, y = 4$

5. $x = 4, y = 5$ **6.** $x = 5, y = -2$

7. $x = 6, y = -3$ **8.** $x = 7, y = -2$

Exercise 3.1   Page 63

1. $x = 1, y = -1$
2. $x = 1\ y = 3$
3. $x = 3, y = 1$
4. $x = 4, y = -1$
5. $x = 2, y = -1$
6. $x = -3, y = -5$
7. $x = 3, y = 1$
8. $x = -1, y = 2$
9. $x = 2, y = -1$
10. $x = 4, y = -2$
11. $x = -3, y = 4$
12. $x = 2, y = -3$
13. $x = 1, y = -3$
14. $x = 2, y = -5$
15. $x = 2, y = 7$
16. $x = 2, y = -2$
17. $x = 1, y = -2$
18. $x = 5, y = 3$
19. $x = 1, y = -2$
20. $x = 2, y = -2$
21. $x = \frac{11}{3}, y = \frac{2}{3}$
22. $x = \frac{6}{5}, y = \frac{8}{5}$
23. $x = 1, y = -1$
24. $x = \frac{21}{5}, y = -\frac{9}{5}$
25. $x = 1, y = -1$
26. $x = -\frac{1}{2}, y = -3$
27. $x = \frac{4}{3}, y = \frac{2}{3}$
28. $x = -7, y = 6$
29. $x = \frac{4}{3}, y = \frac{11}{3}$
30. $x = \frac{13}{7}, y = -\frac{4}{7}$
31. $x = -\frac{3}{4}, y = \frac{1}{4}$
32. $x = \frac{3}{8}, y = \frac{1}{2}$
33. $x = -\frac{2}{3}, y = -\frac{8}{3}$
34. $x = -\frac{5}{3}, y = -\frac{26}{3}$
35. $x = \frac{1}{3}, = \frac{2}{3}$
36. $x = -\frac{9}{11}, y = -\frac{4}{11}$
37. $x = -19, y = -32$
38. $x = \frac{9}{10}, y = -\frac{3}{10}$
39. $x = \frac{14}{11}, y = -\frac{27}{11}$
40. $x = -\frac{2}{17}, y = -\frac{10}{17}$

Chapter 7

Exercise 2.1   Page 66

1. $c = a - b$
2. $b = a - c$
3. $g = x - c$
4. $d = y + c$
5. $s = b - r$
6. $s = t + r$
7. $d = g - s$
8. $a = d + c$
9. $y = a + g$
10. $d = a + t$
11. $n = j - d$
12. $v = h - s$
13. $e = r - a$
14. $m = w - k$
15. $c = b - e$
16. $y = z - x$
17. $v = z - a$
18. $j = r - a$
19. $s = e - h$
20. $v = s - r$
21. $t = k - m$
22. $b = v - f$
23. $c = a - h$
24. $m = n - u$

Exercise 2.2   Page 66

1. $c = \frac{a}{b}$
2. $b = \frac{a}{c}$
3. $g = \frac{x}{c}$
4. $d = \frac{y}{c}$
5. $s = \frac{b}{r}$
6. $s = \frac{t}{r}$
7. $d = \frac{g}{s}$
8. $c = \frac{d}{4}$
9. $y = \frac{a}{g}$
10. $t = \frac{a}{6}$
11. $n = \frac{j}{2}$
12. $v = \frac{h}{3}$
13. $e = \frac{a}{4}$
14. $m = \frac{w}{5}$
15. $c = \frac{e}{b}$
16. $y = \frac{z}{3x}$
17. $v = \frac{z}{2b}$
18. $j = \frac{a}{r}$
19. $s = \frac{e}{6}$
20. $v = \frac{r}{s}$
21. $k = \frac{m}{2t}$
22. $c = \frac{f}{10b}$
23. $c = \frac{a}{8h}$
24. $n = \frac{u}{7m}$

Exercise 2.3   Page 67

1. $c = ax$
2. $b = ds$
3. $g = hw$
4. $d = 3n$
5. $s = 6e$
6. $e = uw$
7. $d = 4aq$
8. $c = 2pr$
9. $y = 5bu$
10. $t = \frac{w}{a}$
11. $n = \frac{x}{g}$
12. $v = \frac{z}{k}$
13. $e = \frac{3x}{c}$
14. $m = \frac{2x}{j}$
15. $c = \frac{5t}{a}$
16. $a = \frac{bc}{2}$
17. $v = \frac{3dm}{4x}$
18. $j = \frac{3x}{2t}$
19. $r = \frac{5x}{4a}$
20. $b = \frac{7ax}{3ch}$
21. $u = \frac{4brs}{5x}$
22. $c = \frac{5aby}{2d}$
23. $d = \frac{4cgt}{3b}$
24. $x = \frac{2abc}{yz}$

Exercise 2.4   Page 68

1. $b = \sqrt{a}$
2. $a = \sqrt{c}$
3. $g = \sqrt[3]{x}$
4. $d = \sqrt[4]{y}$
5. $s = b^2$
6. $r = t^2$
7. $d = g^2$
8. $c = \sqrt[5]{d}$
9. $y = a^3$
10. $t = a^5$
11. $n = j^7$
12. $v = \sqrt[5]{h}$
13. $e = a^2$
14. $m = \sqrt[3]{w}$
15. $c = e^6$

Exercise 2.5   Page 68

1. $m = \frac{y-c}{x}$
2. $x = \frac{d+u}{3}$
3. $t = \frac{h-v}{5}$
4. $b = \frac{n+r}{x}$
5. $n = \frac{e-b}{m}$
6. $r = \frac{w+xy}{t}$
7. $g = \sqrt{\frac{q}{r}}$
8. $t = \sqrt{\frac{p}{6}}$
9. $g = \sqrt[3]{\frac{b}{4}}$
10. $x = \frac{a^2}{6}$
11. $c = \frac{g^3}{3}$
12. $v = \left(\frac{k}{6}\right)^2$
13. $e = \frac{\sqrt{c}}{2}$
14. $x = jm - a$
15. $t = ah + r$
16. $a = cd + 3b$
17. $v = dm + a$
18. $x = 2t^2$
19. $r = \sqrt[3]{4a}$
20. $b = c(h - r)$
21. $u = 2b(s + g)$
22. $c = (y - e)^3$
23. $d = \sqrt[3]{t + u}$
24. $x = c^4 - 3e$

Exercise 2.6   Page 69

1. $t = \sqrt{\frac{a-b}{3}}$
2. $r = \sqrt[3]{\frac{d+b}{g}}$
3. $g = eh^2 + 2$
4. $d = n^3 w + b$
5. $s = \sqrt{en + m}$
6. $e = \sqrt{wr + x}$
7. $d = \sqrt[3]{\frac{q+2e}{4}}$
8. $r = \sqrt{\frac{c}{2p}}$
9. $y = \sqrt[3]{\frac{5bu+d}{4}}$
10. $t = \frac{a}{e-1}$
11. $n = \sqrt{2gr - w}$
12. $v = \frac{k}{r+1}$
13. $e = \frac{3x}{c-a}$
14. $m = \frac{2x}{j+b}$
15. $c = \frac{e-b}{a^3}$
16. $a = \sqrt[3]{\frac{n-m}{3}}$
17. $v = \frac{m^2}{25} + 2b$
18. $j = \frac{c+t}{d-1}$

19. $r = \sqrt{dep + s}$ 20. $b = \sqrt{\dfrac{r+d}{4}}$ 21. $u = k^3 v + r$

22. $v = \dfrac{b^2}{9} - 4e$ 23. $y = \sqrt[3]{\dfrac{4r-e}{ac}}$ 24. $x = \dfrac{y+m}{a-1}$

Exercise 2.7   Page 70

1. $h = \dfrac{V}{\pi r^2}$ 2. $h = \dfrac{3V}{\pi r^2}$ 3. $r = \sqrt[3]{\dfrac{3V}{4\pi}}$

4. $r = \sqrt{\dfrac{A}{4\pi}}$ 5. $r = \sqrt{\dfrac{V}{\pi h}}$ 6. $r = \sqrt{\dfrac{3V}{\pi h}}$

Chapter 8

Exercise 2.1   Page 72

1. $\dfrac{1}{4}$ 2. 10 3. 8 4. $\dfrac{1}{5}$

5. $\dfrac{1}{3}$ 6. $\dfrac{1}{2}$ 7. 8 8. 7

9. $\dfrac{2}{r}$ 10. $3h$ 11. $\dfrac{1}{2j}$ 12. $\dfrac{m}{2}$

13. 3 14. $\dfrac{r}{5}$ 15. $\dfrac{1}{2n}$ 16. $\dfrac{1}{9}$

17. 3 18. $\dfrac{1}{4}$ 19. $\dfrac{1}{7}$ 20. $\dfrac{3}{4}$

21. 5 22. $\dfrac{2}{3}$ 23. $\dfrac{1}{5}$ 24. $\dfrac{3}{2}$

24. k 26. $\dfrac{1}{m}$ 27. p 28. r

29. $\dfrac{1}{v}$ 30. $\dfrac{1}{xy}$ 31. $\dfrac{4a}{5}$ 32. $\dfrac{2}{5c}$

33. $\dfrac{2}{d}$ 34. $\dfrac{4}{f}$ 35. $\dfrac{1}{4h}$ 36. $\dfrac{x}{20}$

37. $\dfrac{4b}{3}$ 38. y 39. $\dfrac{1}{a}$ 40. $\dfrac{3bc}{5}$

41. $\dfrac{2f}{3d}$ 42. $\dfrac{3b^2}{c}$ 43. $\dfrac{3x}{4}$ 44. $\dfrac{5su}{62t}$

45. $\dfrac{4}{7mp}$

Exercise 2.2A   Page 73

1. $\dfrac{1}{a+1}$ 2. $a+2$ 3. $x-2$ 4. $\dfrac{1}{4d-1}$

5. $\dfrac{1}{2e+3}$ 6. $\dfrac{1}{2f-1}$ 7. $2g-4$ 8. $h-3$

9. $\dfrac{5}{2j-k}$ 10. $\dfrac{3}{2k-6m}$ 11. $\dfrac{4m-5}{10}$ 12. $\dfrac{4n-1}{2}$

13. $\dfrac{n}{4n-2}$ 14. $\dfrac{3p}{5p-2}$ 15. $\dfrac{6n}{7n-3}$ 16. $\dfrac{3a-4}{2a}$

17. $\dfrac{1}{b}$ 18. $\dfrac{1}{c}$ 19. $2d$ 20. $5e$

21. $\dfrac{1}{f-5}$ 22. $g-1$ 23. $\dfrac{1}{h+4}$ 24. $\dfrac{1}{9+r}$

25. $\dfrac{1}{x-4}$ 26. $\dfrac{x-2}{x+1}$ 27. $\dfrac{y+9}{5y}$ 28. $\dfrac{4h-2}{5h}$

29. $\dfrac{5z}{20z-7}$ 30. $-\dfrac{1}{3}$ 31. $\dfrac{1}{x-5}$ 32. $6b$

33. $\dfrac{x+3}{x+5}$ 34. $\dfrac{y+3}{y-9}$ 35. $-\dfrac{1}{5}$ 36. $\dfrac{x+6}{x-3}$

Exercise 2.2B   Page 74

1. $\dfrac{x}{x+6}$ 2. $\dfrac{x+1}{x-1}$ 3. $\dfrac{x}{x-4}$ 4. $\dfrac{x-4}{x}$

5. $\dfrac{x-5}{x-2}$ 6. $\dfrac{x-8}{x}$ 7. $\dfrac{x-4}{x+3}$ 8. $\dfrac{x-4}{x}$

9. $\dfrac{x+3}{x-3}$ 10. $\dfrac{x+5}{x}$ 11. $\dfrac{x}{x-1}$ 12. $\dfrac{6}{x-2}$

13. $\dfrac{x-4}{4}$ 14. $\dfrac{x}{7}$ 15. $\dfrac{x+3}{x+2}$ 16. $\dfrac{x-10}{x+3}$

17. $\dfrac{x-4}{x+10}$ 18. $\dfrac{x+9}{x-8}$ 19. $\dfrac{2x+3}{x+3}$ 20. $\dfrac{x-4}{3x-4}$

21. $\dfrac{2+x}{7+x}$ 22. $\dfrac{2x-3}{2(x-2)}$ 23. $\dfrac{3+x}{3(4-x)}$ 24. $\dfrac{1-2x}{4(5-x)}$

Exercise 2.3   Page 75

1. $\dfrac{ac}{bd}$ 2. $\dfrac{ce}{df}$ 3. $\dfrac{g^2}{hk}$ 4. $\dfrac{su}{t^2}$

5. $\dfrac{z}{y}$ 6. $\dfrac{a}{c}$ 7. a 8. $\dfrac{1}{mn}$

9. $\dfrac{uz}{y}$ 10. $\dfrac{1}{v}$ 11. $\dfrac{t}{d}$ 12. $\dfrac{1}{bk}$

13. 2 14. $\dfrac{1}{4}$ 15. $\dfrac{2n}{3}$ 16. $\dfrac{6}{c}$

17. $\dfrac{2s}{u}$ 18. $\dfrac{s}{2t}$ 19. $\dfrac{c^2}{6bd}$ 20. $\dfrac{1}{2}$

21. $\dfrac{28a^2}{15bc}$ 22. $\dfrac{2c^2}{3d^2}$ 23. $\dfrac{3a}{5c}$ 24. $\dfrac{2z}{7y}$

25. $\dfrac{rt}{6s}$ 26. $\dfrac{v^2}{9uw}$ 27. $\dfrac{4f}{eg}$ 28. $\dfrac{4x^2y}{z^2}$

29. $\dfrac{4a^2}{5}$ 30. $\dfrac{9w^2}{2}$ 31. $\dfrac{4svw}{7t}$ 32. $\dfrac{5x^3}{18y^2}$

33. $\dfrac{3c}{7d}$ 34. $\dfrac{1}{3v^2}$ 35. $\dfrac{5}{24x^2y}$ 36. $\dfrac{8}{9x}$

Exercise 2.4   Page 76

1. $\dfrac{ad}{bc}$ 2. $\dfrac{cf}{de}$ 3. $\dfrac{k}{h}$ 4. $\dfrac{s}{u}$

5. $\dfrac{z}{y}$ 6. 1 7. $\dfrac{ac}{b}$ 8. $\dfrac{1}{mn}$

9. $\dfrac{uz}{y}$ 10. $\dfrac{1}{v}$ 11. $\dfrac{t}{d}$ 12. $\dfrac{1}{kb}$

13. 4 14. $\dfrac{1}{3}$ 15. $\dfrac{4n}{5}$ 16. $\dfrac{c}{4}$

17. $\dfrac{su}{3t^2}$ 18. $\dfrac{5s}{6}$ 19. $\dfrac{2ec}{3ab}$ 20. $\dfrac{27c}{25d}$

21. $\dfrac{c}{b}$ 22. $\dfrac{5}{2c}$ 23. $\dfrac{4a}{3}$ 24. $2xy$

25. $\dfrac{15rt}{7}$ 26. $\dfrac{8v^2}{uw}$ 27. $\dfrac{4g}{75}$ 28. $\dfrac{2x^2y}{5z}$

29. $\dfrac{x+1}{2}$ 30. $\dfrac{2(x-2)}{x}$ 31. $16(x+2)$ 32. $\dfrac{5}{(x+3)(x+1)}$

33. $\dfrac{x+1}{2}$ 34. $\dfrac{1}{x-1}$ 35. $\dfrac{1}{2(x+4)}$ 36. 1

1. $\dfrac{7}{b}$ 2. $\dfrac{11}{d}$ 3. $\dfrac{3+g}{a}$ 4. $\dfrac{7+u}{t}$

5. $\dfrac{3}{y}$ 6. $\dfrac{4}{b}$ 7. $\dfrac{6-a}{c}$ 8. $\dfrac{t-n}{m}$

9. $\dfrac{3z+2y}{yz}$ 10. $\dfrac{4c-b}{bc}$ 11. $\dfrac{2e+4d}{de}$ 12. $\dfrac{b-3c}{cb}$

13. $\dfrac{8+2cd}{d^2}$ 14. $\dfrac{4-r}{r^2}$ 15. $\dfrac{3c+2}{c^2}$ 16. $\dfrac{6-b}{2b^2}$

17. $\dfrac{9u+2t}{6tu}$ 18. $\dfrac{15t-12r}{20rt}$ 19. $\dfrac{63c+8b}{9bc}$ 20. $\dfrac{9b-10a}{12ab}$

21. $\dfrac{2ac+12ab}{9bc}$ 22. $\dfrac{c-30d}{5d^2}$ 23. $\dfrac{3a+36ab^2}{4b^3}$ 24. $\dfrac{6x^2y-3x}{7y^2}$

25. $\dfrac{9+55st}{15s^2}$ 26. $\dfrac{55s-16r}{60rs}$ 27. $\dfrac{16e+9ag}{24eg}$ 28. $\dfrac{9bx-2cz}{24xz}$

29. $\dfrac{5c+2ad}{abc}$ 30. $\dfrac{5z-3wx}{xyz}$ 31. $\dfrac{2t^2+3r}{rst}$ 32. $\dfrac{5e-c^2d}{cd^2e}$

1. $\dfrac{7x-4}{x(x-1)}$ 2. $\dfrac{11x+15}{x(x+3)}$ 3. $\dfrac{5x+2}{6}$ 4. $\dfrac{9x-8}{x(x-4)}$

5. $\dfrac{x-8}{12}$ 6. $\dfrac{4x-10}{x(x+5)}$ 7. $\dfrac{-4x-3}{x(x-3)}$ 8. $\dfrac{x+10}{x(x-5)}$

9. $\dfrac{5x-8}{(x-1)(x-2)}$ 10. $\dfrac{3x+18}{(x+2)(x+5)}$ 11. $\dfrac{3x-1}{4}$ 12. $\dfrac{-x+13}{20}$

13. $\dfrac{5x+5}{(x-5)(x+5)}$ 14. $\dfrac{3x+5}{(x-1)(x+1)}$ 15. $\dfrac{5x+4}{(x-4)(x+4)}$ 16. $\dfrac{2x-12}{(x-3)(x+3)}$

17. $\dfrac{7x+18}{12}$ 18. $\dfrac{-2x}{(x-3)(x-5)}$ 19. $\dfrac{15x+47}{(x-2)(x+9)}$ 20. $\dfrac{x+19}{12}$

21. $\dfrac{4x-1}{(x-1)(x+1)}$ 22. $\dfrac{-3x-5}{(x-2)(x+2)}$ 23. $\dfrac{2x+9}{(x-3)(x+3)}$ 24. $\dfrac{6x-32}{(x-5)(x+5)}$

Chapter 9

1. $(x+1)^2+2$ 2. $(x-1)^2+3$

3. $(x-2)^2+1$ 4. $(x-2)^2+2$

5. $(x-3)^2+1$ 6. $(x+2)^2+6$

7. $(x-3)^2+3$ 8. $(x+5)^2+5$

9. $(x-4)^2+9$ 10. $(x+5)^2+2$

11. $(x-3)^2-11$ 12. $(x-6)^2-29$

13. $(x+8)^2-71$ 14. $(x-4)^2-20$

15. $(x-5)^2-20$ 16. $(x+8)^2-32$

17. $(x-9)^2-76$ 18. $(x+10)^2-97$

19. $(x+15)^2-231$ 20. $(x+11)^2-142$

21. $(x-8)^2-76$ 22. $(x+6)^2-50$

23. $(x-8)^2-91$ 24. $(x+10)^2-90$

25. $(x-20)^2-435$ 26. $(x-15)^2-250$

27. $(x+4)^2-22$ 28. $(x+9)^2-93$

29. $(x-7)^2-65$ 30. $(x-15)^2-249$

1. $\left(x+\dfrac{3}{2}\right)^2+\dfrac{3}{4}$ 2. $\left(x-\dfrac{5}{2}\right)^2+\dfrac{7}{4}$

3. $\left(x-\dfrac{7}{2}\right)^2-\dfrac{29}{4}$ 4. $\left(x-\dfrac{5}{2}\right)^2-\dfrac{1}{4}$

5. $\left(x-\dfrac{3}{2}\right)^2+\dfrac{31}{4}$ 6. $\left(x+\dfrac{9}{2}\right)^2-\dfrac{41}{4}$

7. $\left(x-\dfrac{7}{2}\right)^2-\dfrac{5}{4}$ 8. $\left(x+\dfrac{9}{2}\right)^2+\dfrac{39}{4}$

9. $\left(x-\dfrac{7}{2}\right)^2+\dfrac{51}{4}$ 10. $\left(x+\dfrac{1}{2}\right)^2+\dfrac{107}{4}$

11. $\left(x-\dfrac{11}{2}\right)^2-\dfrac{129}{4}$ 12. $\left(x-\dfrac{1}{2}\right)^2+\dfrac{27}{4}$

13. $\left(x+\dfrac{9}{2}\right)^2-\dfrac{109}{4}$ 14. $\left(x-\dfrac{11}{2}\right)^2-\dfrac{137}{4}$

15. $\left(x-\dfrac{13}{2}\right)^2-\dfrac{149}{4}$ 16. $\left(x+\dfrac{7}{2}\right)^2+\dfrac{79}{4}$

17. $\left(x-\dfrac{5}{2}\right)^2-\dfrac{5}{4}$ 18. $\left(x+\dfrac{7}{2}\right)^2-\dfrac{37}{4}$

19. $\left(x+\dfrac{13}{2}\right)^2-\dfrac{193}{4}$ 20. $\left(x+\dfrac{15}{2}\right)^2-\dfrac{309}{4}$

21. $\left(x-\dfrac{11}{2}\right)^2-\dfrac{165}{4}$ 22. $\left(x+\dfrac{15}{2}\right)^2-\dfrac{281}{4}$

23. $\left(x-\dfrac{5}{2}\right)^2-\dfrac{133}{4}$ 24. $\left(x-\dfrac{3}{2}\right)^2+\dfrac{27}{4}$

25. $\left(x-\dfrac{5}{2}\right)^2-\dfrac{165}{4}$ 26. $\left(x-\dfrac{7}{2}\right)^2-\dfrac{149}{4}$

27. $\left(x-\dfrac{9}{2}\right)^2-\dfrac{105}{4}$ 28. $\left(x+\dfrac{3}{2}\right)^2-\dfrac{65}{4}$

29. $\left(x-\dfrac{11}{2}\right)^2-\dfrac{185}{4}$ 30. $\left(x-\dfrac{5}{2}\right)^2-\dfrac{117}{4}$

1. $2\left(x+\dfrac{3}{2}\right)^2+\dfrac{9}{2}$ 2. $2(x-2)^2-1$

3. $3(x-1)^2+2$ 4. $4(x-1)^2+7$

5. $3(x-2)^2+4$ 6. $4(x+2)^2+3$

7. $3(x-4)^2-17$ 8. $2(x+3)^2+15$

9. $4(x-1)^2+21$ 10. $7(x+1)^2+22$

11. $6(x-1)^2-8$ 12. $9(x-1)^2+62$

13. $12\left(x+\dfrac{3}{2}\right)^2-28$ 14. $20(x-1)^2-24$

15. $6(x-2)^2+35$ 16. $3\left(x+\dfrac{3}{2}\right)^2+\dfrac{97}{4}$

17. $2\left(x-\dfrac{3}{2}\right)^2+\dfrac{1}{2}$ 18. $4\left(x-\dfrac{3}{2}\right)^2+8$

19. $6\left(x+\dfrac{3}{2}\right)^2-\dfrac{39}{4}$ 20. $5\left(x+\dfrac{3}{2}\right)^2-\dfrac{49}{4}$

21. $8\left(x-\dfrac{3}{2}\right)^2-31$ 22. $2\left(x+\dfrac{5}{2}\right)^2-\dfrac{27}{2}$

23. $3\left(x-\dfrac{7}{2}\right)^2-\dfrac{263}{4}$ 24. $4\left(x+\dfrac{5}{2}\right)^2-14$

25. $8\left(x-\dfrac{5}{2}\right)^2-85$ 26. $10\left(x-\dfrac{3}{2}\right)^2-\dfrac{91}{2}$

27. $7\left(x+\dfrac{5}{2}\right)^2-\dfrac{199}{4}$ 28. $11\left(x+\dfrac{3}{2}\right)^2-\dfrac{155}{4}$

29. $9\left(x-\dfrac{3}{2}\right)^2-\dfrac{233}{4}$ 30. $6\left(x-\dfrac{7}{2}\right)^2-\dfrac{197}{2}$

1. $-(x+1)^2+5$ 2. $-(x+1)^2+11$

3. $-(x-1)^2+2$ 4. $-(x+1)^2+8$

5. $-(x+3)^2+10$ 6. $-(x+1)^2+3$

7. $-(x-2)^2+10$ 8. $-(x-3)^2+14$

9. $-(x+3)^2+14$ 10. $-(x+4)^2+23$

11. $-(x-5)^2+30$ 12. $-(x+3)^2+22$

13. $-(x-5)^2 + 27$
15. $-(x-7)^2 + 53$
17. $-\left(x+\frac{3}{2}\right)^2 + \frac{13}{4}$
19. $-3(x+1)^2 + 4$
21. $-3(x-2)^2 + 16$
23. $-2\left(x+\frac{3}{2}\right)^2 + \frac{31}{2}$
25. $-5\left(x-\frac{1}{2}\right)^2 + \frac{13}{4}$
27. $-2\left(x+\frac{5}{2}\right)^2 + \frac{31}{2}$
29. $-2\left(x+\frac{3}{2}\right)^2 + \frac{35}{2}$

14. $-(x+6)^2 + 53$
16. $-2(x+1)^2 + 5$
18. $-\left(x-\frac{5}{2}\right)^2 + \frac{69}{4}$
20. $-2(x+1)^2 + 7$
22. $-3\left(x+\frac{3}{2}\right)^2 + \frac{47}{4}$
24. $-4\left(x-\frac{3}{2}\right)^2 + 20$
26. $-4\left(x+\frac{1}{2}\right)^2 + 6$
28. $-4\left(x-\frac{3}{2}\right)^2 + 14$
30. $-5\left(x-\frac{5}{2}\right)^2 + \frac{129}{4}$

Chapter 10

Exercise 2.1A   Page 85
1. $x=0, x=1$
2. $x=0, x=-2$
3. $x=0, x=-1$
4. $x=0, x=2$
5. $x=0, x=-3$
6. $x=0, x=-5$
7. $x=0, x=-6$
8. $x=0, x=9$
9. $x=0, x=-5$
10. $x=0, x=-1$
11. $x=0, x=\frac{5}{3}$
12. $x=0, x=-\frac{3}{2}$
13. $x=0, x=-\frac{1}{2}$
14. $x=0, x=-\frac{2}{3}$
15. $x=0, x=-\frac{3}{7}$
16. $x=0, x=-\frac{1}{5}$
17. $x=0, x=\frac{1}{2}$
18. $x=0, x=-\frac{2}{9}$

Exercise 2.1B   Page 86
1. $x=5, x=2$
2. $x=4, x=1$
3. $x=-3, x=4$
4. $x=-7, x=-1$
5. $x=-6, x=-3$
6. $x=9, x=-1$
7. $x=-4, x=3$
8. $x=-5, x=3$
9. $x=-2, x=2$
10. $x=5, x=1$
11. $x=3, x=-9$
12. $x=-8, x=1$
13. $x=\frac{2}{3}, x=-3$
14. $x=\frac{3}{4}, x=1$
15. $x=-\frac{3}{4}, x=-2$
16. $x=2, x=-\frac{3}{2}$
17. $x=\frac{3}{2}, x=-2$
18. $x=-\frac{5}{2}, x=1$
19. $x=7, x=-9$
20. $x=-\frac{1}{2}, x=3$
21. $x=\frac{3}{2}, x=-2$
22. $x=-\frac{5}{2}, x=-9$
23. $x=-\frac{5}{2}, x=\frac{1}{2}$
24. $x=-\frac{2}{3}, x=\frac{3}{2}$

Exercise 2.2A   Page 86
1. $x=0, x=-5$
2. $x=0, x=4$
3. $x=0, x=-7$
4. $x=0, x=-2$
5. $x=0, x=5$
6. $x=0, x=10$
7. $x=0, x=-6$
8. $x=0, x=-3$
9. $x=0, x=1$
10. $x=0, x=-4$
11. $x=0, x=5$
12. $x=0, x=-2$
13. $x=0, x=3$
14. $x=0, x=25$
15. $x=0, x=9$
16. $x=0, x=12$
17. $x=0, x=50$
18. $x=0, x=4$

Exercise 2.2B   Page 87
1. $x=1, x=-1$
2. $x=3, x=-3$
3. $x=2, x=-2$
4. $x=4, x=-4$
5. $x=5, x=-5$
6. $x=6, x=-6$
7. $x=7, x=-7$
8. $x=9, x=-9$
9. $x=10, x=-10$
10. $x=1, x=-1$
11. $x=3, x=-3$
12. $x=5, x=-5$
13. $x=\frac{1}{3}, x=-\frac{1}{3}$
14. $x=\frac{2}{5}, x=-\frac{2}{5}$
15. $x=\frac{1}{2}, x=-\frac{1}{2}$

Exercise 2.2C   Page 87
1. $x=-2, x=-3$
2. $x=-6, x=-6$
3. $x=-4, x=3$
4. $x=2, x=8$
5. $x=3, x=8$
6. $x=-2, x=3$
7. $x=3, x=6$
8. $x=6, x=7$
9. $x=4, x=4$
10. $x=-6, x=5$
11. $x=-8, x=2$
12. $x=4, x=6$
13. $x=-7, x=8$
14. $x=-12, x=-3$
15. $x=-6, x=2$

Exercise 2.2D   Page 87
1. $x=-3, x=0$
2. $x=0, x=9$
3. $x=-1, x=1$
4. $x=1, x=7$
5. $x=-1, x=3$
6. $x=-3, x=2$
7. $x=-2, x=2$
8. $x=-2, x=0$
9. $x=-\frac{5}{3}, x=1$
10. $x=5, x=8$
11. $x=3, x=3$
12. $x=-3, x=7$
13. $x=-8, x=9$
14. $x=-3, x=2$
15. $x=-3, x=8$
16. $x=-5, x=0$
17. $x=-6, x=2$
18. $x=1, x=10$
19. $x=-2, x=2$
20. $x=-2, x=3$
21. $x=0, x=3$
22. $x=-6, x=-2$
23. $x=\frac{1}{2}, x=3$
24. $x=-5, x=5$
25. $x=-5, x=5$
26. $x=6, x=9$
27. $x=-2, x=2$
28. $x=-\frac{3}{2}, x=\frac{9}{2}$
29. $x=-3, x=5$
30. $x=-6, x=\frac{5}{3}$

Exercise 2.3   Page 88
1. $x=0, x=3$
2. $x=-4, x=4$
3. $x=0, x=4$
4. $x=1, x=7$
5. $x=3, x=4$
6. $x=-1, x=1$
7. $x=0, x=2$
8. $x=0, x=12$
9. $x=1, x=1$
10. $x=5, x=8$
11. $x=-3, x=-3$
12. $x=-3, x=7$
13. $x=-8, x=9$
14. $x=-1, x=6$
15. $x=-3, x=8$
16. $x=0, x=4$
17. $x=-6, x=2$
18. $x=-6, x=3$
19. $x=-\frac{3}{2}, x=4$
20. $x=-\frac{1}{3}, x=2$
21. $x=\frac{1}{5}, x=3$
22. $x=-2, x=6$
23. $x=-5, x=2$
24. $x=1, x=6$
25. $x=2, x=3$
26. $x=-3, x=10$
27. $x=2, x=6$
28. $x=-1, x=\frac{15}{2}$
29. $x=-2, x=5$
30. $x=-2, x=\frac{4}{5}$

Exercise 2.4   Page 89

1. $x = -5.2, x = 1.2$
2. $x = -4.2, x = 0.7$
3. $x = -4.4, x = 0.4$
4. $x = 0.7, x = 4.3$
5. $x = 0.8, x = 5.2$
6. $x = -0.6, x = 3.6$
7. $x = -10.1, x = 1.1$
8. $x = -5.6, x = -0.9$
9. $x = -0.2, x = 8.2$
10. $x = -9.6, x = 0.6$
11. $x = -9.6, x = 1.6$
12. $x = -3.6, x = 0.3$
13. $x = -4.4, x = -0.1$
14. $x = -1.7, x = 1.7$
15. $x = -0.2, x = 4.2$
16. $x = -9.5, x = 0.5$
17. $x = -5.2, x = 0.2$
18. $x = -10.6, x = 0.6$
19. $x = -0.1, x = 7.1$
20. $x = 0.4, x = 2.6$
21. $x = 0.3, x = 3.7$
22. $x = 0.2, x = 4.3$
23. $x = -4.2, x = 0.2$
24. $x = -3.5, x = 0.2$
25. $x = -0.2, x = 2.9$
26. $x = -0.2, x = 4.6$
27. $x = 0.3, x = 0.7$
28. $x = -0.1, x = 3.8$
29. $x = -0.4, x = 3.4$
30. $x = 0.1, x = 3.9$

Exercise 2.5   Page 91

1. $L = 6cm, B = 2cm$
2. $L = 7cm, B = 4cm$
3. $L = 7cm, B = 2cm$
4. $L = 6cm, B = 4cm$
5. $L = 15cm, B = 4cm$
6. $L = 9cm, B = 4cm$
7. $L = 10cm, B = 2cm$
8. $L = 13cm, B = 6cm$
9. $L = 9cm, B = 7cm$
10. $L = 6cm, B = 3cm$
11. $L = 40cm, B = 2.5cm$
12. $L = 15cm, B = 3cm$
13. $Area = 16cm^2$
14. $Area = 64cm^2$
15. $Area = 64cm^2$
16. $Area = 36cm^2$
17. $Area = 48cm^2$
18. $Area = 6cm^2$
19. $Area = 36cm^2$
20. $L = 16cm, B = 11cm$
21. $L = 14cm, B = 10cm$
22. $Border = 1m$
23. $Frame = 5cm$

Exercise 2.6   Page 95

1. $b^2 - 4ac > 0,$ ∴ there are two real and distinct roots.
2. $b^2 - 4ac < 0,$ ∴ there are no real roots.
3. $b^2 - 4ac > 0,$ ∴ there are two real and distinct roots.
4. $b^2 - 4ac > 0,$ ∴ there are two real and distinct roots.
5. $b^2 - 4ac > 0,$ ∴ there are two real and distinct roots.
6. $b^2 - 4ac < 0,$ ∴ there are no real roots.
7. $b^2 - 4ac > 0,$ ∴ there are two real and distinct roots.
8. $b^2 - 4ac = 0,$ ∴ there are two real and equal roots.
9. $b^2 - 4ac > 0,$ ∴ there are two real and distinct roots.
10. $b^2 - 4ac > 0,$ ∴ there are two real and distinct roots.
11. $b^2 - 4ac < 0,$ ∴ there are no real roots.
12. $b^2 - 4ac > 0,$ ∴ there are two real and distinct roots.
13. $b^2 - 4ac < 0,$ ∴ there are no real roots.
14. $b^2 - 4ac > 0,$ ∴ there are two real and distinct roots.
15. $b^2 - 4ac > 0,$ ∴ there are two real and distinct roots.
16. $b^2 - 4ac > 0,$ ∴ there are two real and distinct roots.
17. $b^2 - 4ac > 0,$ ∴ there are two real and distinct roots.
18. $b^2 - 4ac < 0,$ ∴ there are no real roots.
19. $b^2 - 4ac = 0,$ ∴ there are two real and equal roots.
20. $b^2 - 4ac < 0,$ ∴ there are no real roots.
21. $b^2 - 4ac = 0,$ ∴ there are two real and equal roots.
22. $b^2 - 4ac > 0,$ ∴ there are two real and distinct roots.
23. $b^2 - 4ac < 0,$ ∴ there are no real roots.
24. $b^2 - 4ac > 0,$ ∴ there are two real and distinct roots.

25. $b^2 - 4ac > 0,$ ∴ there are two real and distinct roots.
26. $b^2 - 4ac = 0,$ ∴ there are two real and equal roots.
27. $b^2 - 4ac > 0,$ ∴ there are two real and distinct roots.
28. $b^2 - 4ac = 0,$ ∴ there are two real and equal roots.
29. $b^2 - 4ac > 0,$ ∴ there are two real and distinct roots.
30. $b^2 - 4ac < 0,$ ∴ there are no real roots.

Exercise 2.7   Page 96

1. $k = 9$
2. $k = -4, k = 4$
3. $k = -6, k = 6$
4. $k = 8$
5. $k = -3, k = 3$
6. $k = -4, k = 4$
7. $k = 0, k = 2$
8. $k = 0, k = 5$
9. $k = -2, k = 10$
10. $k = -5, k = 7$
11. $k = 1, k = 13$
12. $k = -9, k = -1$
13. $k = -7, k = 5$
14. $k = 2, k = 6$
15. $k = 1, k = 37$

Exercise 3.1   Page 96

1. $x = -5, x = 1$
2. $x = -5, x = -1$
3. $x = -9, x = -1$
4. $x = 1, x = 7$
5. $x = -1, x = 7$
6. $x = -4, x = 6$
7. $x = -1 - \sqrt{3}$, $x = -1 + \sqrt{3}$
8. $x = -2 - \sqrt{3}$, $x = -2 + \sqrt{3}$
9. $x = -3 - \sqrt{11}$, $x = -3 + \sqrt{11}$
10. $x = 2 - \sqrt{7}$, $x = 2 + \sqrt{7}$
11. $x = -4 - \sqrt{6}$, $x = -4 + \sqrt{6}$
12. $x = 2 - 2\sqrt{3}$, $x = 2 + 2\sqrt{3}$
13. $x = -5 - \sqrt{5}$, $x = -5 + \sqrt{5}$
14. $x = 3 - 2\sqrt{3}$, $x = 3 + 2\sqrt{3}$
15. $x = 2 - 2\sqrt{6}$, $x = 2 + 2\sqrt{6}$
16. $x = -1 - \sqrt{2}$, $x = -1 + \sqrt{2}$
17. $x = 6 - 3\sqrt{2}$, $x = 6 + 3\sqrt{2}$
18. $x = -4 - 2\sqrt{3}$, $x = -4 + 2\sqrt{3}$
19. $x = 4 - 2\sqrt{6}$, $x = 4 + 2\sqrt{6}$
20. $x = \frac{2-\sqrt{2}}{2}$, $x = \frac{2+\sqrt{2}}{2}$
21. $x = \frac{-3-\sqrt{11}}{2}$, $x = \frac{-3+\sqrt{11}}{2}$
22. $x = \frac{4-\sqrt{13}}{2}$, $x = \frac{4+\sqrt{13}}{2}$
23. $x = \frac{-6-\sqrt{42}}{2}$, $x = \frac{-6+\sqrt{42}}{2}$
24. $x = -3 - 2\sqrt{2}$, $x = -3 + 2\sqrt{2}$
25. $x = \frac{6-\sqrt{42}}{3}$, $x = \frac{6+\sqrt{42}}{3}$
26. $x = \frac{-3-\sqrt{21}}{3}$, $x = \frac{-3+\sqrt{21}}{3}$
27. $x = \frac{-10-\sqrt{105}}{5}$, $x = \frac{-10+\sqrt{105}}{5}$
28. $x = \frac{12-\sqrt{138}}{6}$, $x = \frac{12+\sqrt{138}}{6}$
29. $x = \frac{-8-\sqrt{58}}{4}$, $x = \frac{-8+\sqrt{58}}{4}$
30. $x = \frac{-18-\sqrt{327}}{3}$, $x = \frac{-18+\sqrt{327}}{3}$

Exercise 3.2   Page 97

1. $-3 < x < 0$
2. $x < 0, x > 8$
3. $-2 \leq x \leq 2$
4. $x \leq 1, x \geq 7$
5. $-1 < x < 3$
6. $x < -3, x > 2$
7. $-3 < x < 3$
8. $x \leq -2, x \geq 0$
9. $x < -4, x > 2$
10. $-2 \leq x \leq 3$
11. $-2 < x < 6$
12. $-3 < x < 7$
13. $x < -4, x > 9$
14. $x < -4, x > 1$
15. $-1 \leq x \leq 6$
16. $-6 \leq x \leq 0$
17. $x < -12, x > 1$
18. $1 \leq x \leq 10$
19. $x < -2, x > 2$
20. $x \leq -3, x \geq 2$
21. $0 < x < 2$
22. $-3 \leq x \leq -2$
23. $x < 1, x > 6$
24. $-5 \leq x \leq 5$
25. $x < -\sqrt{3}, x > \sqrt{3}$
26. $3 < x < 12$
27. $-\sqrt{2} < x < \sqrt{2}$
28. $-3 < x < 6$
29. $-3 < x < 5$
30. $x \leq -12, x \geq 1$

Exercise 3.3   Page 98

1. $x = -3, x = 2$
2. $no\ real\ solutions$
3. $x = -2, x = 1$
4. $x = 3 - \sqrt{3},\ x = 3 + \sqrt{3}$
5. $x = -7, x = 1$
6. $x = -1, x = 3$
7. $x = -5 - 5\sqrt{2},\ x = -5 + 5\sqrt{2}$
8. $x = -5, x = 5$
9. $x = -1, x = 4$
10. $x = -3 - \sqrt{19},\ x = -3 + \sqrt{19}$
11. $x = -5, x = -3$
12. $x < 3, x > 5$
13. $x = -\frac{\sqrt{2}}{2}, x = \frac{\sqrt{2}}{2}$
14. $x = -\frac{\sqrt{3}}{2}, x = \frac{\sqrt{3}}{2}$
15. $x = 2 - \sqrt{5},\ x = 2 + \sqrt{5}$
16. $x \leq -\sqrt{5}, x \geq \sqrt{5}$
17. $x = -2 - \sqrt{5},\ x = -2 + \sqrt{5}$
18. $x = -4, x = -3$
19. $x = -1, x = 7$
20. $no\ real\ solutions$
21. $no\ real\ solutions$
22. $x = \frac{-2-\sqrt{5}}{2}, x = \frac{-2+\sqrt{5}}{2}$
23. $x = 0, x = 1$
24. $x = \frac{-3-\sqrt{30}}{3}, x = \frac{-3+\sqrt{30}}{3}$
25. $x = \frac{3-\sqrt{3}}{3}, x = \frac{3+\sqrt{3}}{3}$
26. $no\ real\ solutions$
27. $x = \frac{5-\sqrt{5}}{10}, x = \frac{5+\sqrt{5}}{10}$
28. $x = 4 - 4\sqrt{2},\ x = 4 + 4\sqrt{2}$
29. $x = -6 - 6\sqrt{2},\ x = -6 + 6\sqrt{2}$
30. $x < -\frac{1}{\sqrt{3}}, x > \frac{1}{\sqrt{3}}$

Chapter 11

Exercise 3.1   Page 100

1. $x = -3, x = -1, x = 1$
2. $x = -4, x = -1, x = 2$
3. $x = -3, x = 2\ twice$
4. $x = -1, x = 2, x = 3$
5. $x = -3, x = 3$
6. $x = -1\ twice, x = 2$
7. $x = 1, x = 2\ twice$
8. $x = -4, x = -2, x = 1$
9. $x = -2, x = 2$
10. $x = -6, x = 2, x = 4$
11. $x = 2\ three\ times$
12. $x = -3, x = \frac{1}{2}, x = 1$
13. $x = -6, x = -3, x = 2$
14. $x = -5, x = 2, x = 4$
15. $x = -2, x = 2\ twice$
16. $x = -4, x = 4$
17. $x = -1, x = 1$
18. $x = -3, x = -2, x = 1$
19. $x = -5, x = -1, x = 5$
20. $x = 1\ three\ times, x = 2$
21. $x = -5, x = 4\ twice$
22. $x = -\frac{1}{2}, x = \frac{1}{2}, x = 1$
23. $x = -4, x = -3, x = 3$
24. $x = -1\ twice, x = 1\ twice$
25. $x = -5, x = -1, x = 2$
26. $x = -3\ twice, x = 1$
27. $x = -1, x = 1, x = 3\ twice$

Exercise 3.2   Page 101

1. $(1, 2), (3, 4)$
2. $(2, -2), (4, 0)$
3. $(1, 4), (5, 8)$
4. $(8, 3), (-2, -7)$
5. $(3, -5)\ twice$
6. $(4, -1), (-5, -10)$
7. $(1, -5)\ twice$
8. $(2, -3), (-3, 2)$
9. $(2, 1), (-2, 5), (-1, 4)$
10. $(1, 3)$
11. $(2, -3), (0, -5), (-3, -8)$
12. $(-2, 1), (0, -1), (2, -3)$
13. $(-1, 0)\ twice, (1, 2)$
14. $(-1, -3), (2, 0), (-2, -4)$
15. $(-1, 2), (2, 5)\ twice$

Exercise 3.3   Page 102

1. $(1, 2)\ twice$
2. $(2, 3), (-3, -2)$
3. $(3, 4), (0, -5)$
4. $(1, -2), (3, 0)$
5. $(2, -5), (5, 2)$
6. $(1, 3), (-3, -5)$
7. $(5, 1), (2, -2)$
8. $(3, -2), (-8, 9)$
9. $(-2, 1)\ twice$
10. $(3, 2), (1, 0)$
11. $(2, -2), (7, 3)$
12. $(3, -4), (1, -6)$
13. $(-1, 4), (-5, 0)$
14. $(-3, -4), (-4, -3)$
15. $(2, -6), (10, 2)$